THE OFFICIAL BOLTON WANDERERS QUIZ BOOK

THE OFFICIAL BOLTON WANDERERS QUIZ BOOK

Compiled by Marc White

Foreword by Phil Gartside

APEX PUBLISHING LTD

First published in hardback in 2008 by

Apex Publishing Ltd
PO Box 7086, Clacton on Sea, Essex, CO15 5WN, England
www.apexpublishing.co.uk

Copyright © 2008 by Marc White
The authors have asserted their moral rights

British Library Cataloguing-in-Publication Data
A catalogue record for this book
is available from the British Library

ISBN: 1-906358-39-7   978-1-906358-39-6

Typeset in 10.5pt Baskerville Old Face

Cover Design: Siobhan Smith

Printed and bound in Great Britain by
Biddles Ltd., King's Lynn, Norfolk

This book is an official product of Bolton Wanderers Football Club.

I would like to dedicate this book to two very special people,
my Granda, John McDermott White, who is sadly no longer with us
and who was a huge admirer of Nat Lofthouse, The Lion of Vienna,
and my Granda Bobby McWilliams who is also sadly no longer with us.
We all still miss you both so very much.
I LOVE YOU.
Your Grandson.

Marc

FOREWORD

I was delighted when Marc contacted me asking if I would write the Foreword to this, his *Official Bolton Wanderers Football Club Quiz Book*.

I am extremely proud to be the Chairman of Bolton Wanderers, a founder member club of the Football League. Our club is steeped in a wonderful tradition that dates back from its formation until the present day. Without doubt, the hey days of the club were the 1920s when Charles Foweraker's magnificent side won the FA Cup three times during the decade. However, many fans will also recall our superb team from the 1950s spearheaded by a local lad named Nat Lofthouse who helped the Trotters win the 1958 FA Cup final.

Nat is a Bolton legend, one of those traditional, but oh-so-very-rare-today, one club career players, who delighted fans across the town with his goal scoring exploits for Bolton Wanderers and up and down the country when he proudly wore the Three Lions shirt for England. Fittingly, Nat is still associated with the club today some 68 years since he first walked through the doors of Burnden Park and serves as our Club President. Of course we have moved grounds since Nat last played for us but I know all Bolton Wanderers fans have their own special memories of Burnden Park which served the club so well for more than a century. Equally, I think our Reebok Stadium is one of the best in the country.

Bolton Wanderers FC has had many fantastic players down the years and it is fitting that so many of them have been included here. Indeed, Marc's book is in many ways a quizzical trip through the history of the club as he has added sections on famous managers, the players, FA Cup triumphs, Wembley Finals, League campaigns and Premier League seasons plus much more.

The Official Bolton Wanderers Football Club Quiz Book is quite simply one of those little gems of a book that makes you proud to be a Trotter. The questions are imaginative, yet testing and will please and tease you in equal measure. It is one of those books you can take down to the pub to test your mates' knowledge of the club, or just simply sit at home and see how much your Dad or Grandad knows about the history of the Trotters. But above all else, it is a book which will further your own knowledge of Bolton Wanderers Football Club.

In closing, I hope you enjoy the book as much as I did and let's hope our team can lead Marc to having to write a few new Chapters for the reprint.

Phil Gartside, Chairman
Bolton Wanderers Football Club

INTRODUCTION

I would like to thank my Dad for coming up with the idea for me to write this book. It is only by researching a topic that you truly understand the subject matter and quite early on in the compilation of this book it was evident that Bolton Wanderers Football Club is steeped in history.

I was unaware of the many wonderful players who passed through Burnden Park and the Reebok Stadium and hope that by including a section on many of them I have helped rekindle your own memories of your favourite players.

Bolton Wanderers Football Club, a founder member of the Football League, has helped shape the English game to what it is today, a multi-million pound global corporation. Not many clubs can say that they have played in every Division of the Football League plus the Premier League but the Trotters certainly can. The club also has its place in FA Cup history by winning the first ever FA Cup Final played at Wembley Stadium.

A great deal of thanks must go to Nigel Sheppard who very kindly took the time to check many of my questions and answers with a view to keeping them as accurate as possible. Nigel's website: *www.geocities.com/nigelsheppard/bwfc/index.html* along with the club's official website: *www.bwfc.premiumtv.co.uk* are superb websites to research all things Trotter-related. I would also like to thank Paul Holliday at Bolton Wanderers for all his help.

Finally, I would like to thank my Mum (Janice) and Dad (John) for helping me with the questions in my book and Mum's patience in proofreading my work as well as my brother (Paul) for his encouragement.

As the legendary Freddie Mercury sang in Queen's magnificent *We are the Champions* song "I thank you all".

Best wishes
Marc White

www.apexpublishing.co.uk

THE HISTORY - I

1.   In what year was the club formed?

2.   By what biblical sounding name was the club first known?

3.   In what year did the club change its name to Bolton
     Wanderers Football Club – 1877, 1878 or 1879?

4.   Bolton were founder members of the Football League in 1888.
     How many other clubs made up the inaugural First Division in
     season 1888-89?

5.   Name any two of the four clubs playing in the Premier League
     in season 2007-08 who played in the inaugural First Division
     season in 1888-89 with Bolton?

6.   How many times has Bolton won the FA Cup?

7.   In what year did Bolton win the FA Cup for the first time?

8.   What was of historical significance about the game in Q7?

9.   In what season did Bolton play Premier League football for the
     first time?

10. In what season did Bolton first taste European football in one
     of the three major European club competitions?

THE KIT

11. What colour were the spots adorning Bolton's white shirt in 1884?

12. In what year did Bolton first print a sponsor's name on their shirts?

13. Can you recall the protective sounding company name that first appeared on Bolton shirts as the club's sponsor?

14. What are the traditional colours of the Bolton shirt and shorts?

15. In what decade did Bolton first trial an all-white kit?

16. Describe the official Bolton Wanderers FC club crest as worn on the shirts.

17. What was removed from the club crest after the club moved to the Reebok Stadium?

18. Can you recall the club's original crest?

19. This superstore sponsored the club shirt from 1986-90. Name the superstore.

20. Can you recall the shirt sponsor's name that adorned the Bolton kit in season 1981-82?

MIXED BAG – I

21. Which member of the club appeared in the SKY TV drama series Dream Team when he played himself in an episode shown in early 2006?

22. Apart from Manchester City with what other "City" did ex-Trotter Asa Hartford win a League Cup winners' medal?

23. Bolton Wanderers won the Premier League Asia Trophy in 2005. Can you name any two of the other three teams that participated in the tournament?

24. In what position did the Trotters finish in the Premier League in season 2004-05 – 5th, 6th or 7th?

25. How many international goals did Jay-Jay Okocha score for Nigeria – 15, 16 or 17?

26. To the nearest 15 minutes what is Nat Lofthouse's scoring ratio for Wanderers in 503 games for the club? In other words, how many minutes on average to goals scored did he net for the club?

27. Can you name the Welsh side where Gary Speed took up a part-time coaching role at their academy in July 2006?

28. After what legendary Bolton Wanderers player is the Bolton Wanderers official club mascot named?

29. Can you name the "Johann" who was allocated the No.42 shirt for the Trotters during the 2007-08 season?

30. When Fulham visited Burnden Park on 30 October 1976 for a Division Two game what was introduced at the ground for the first time in the club's history?

BOLTON WANDERERS
v PRESTON NORTH END

31.   Up to the end of the 2007-08 season how many times has
       Bolton met Preston North End at home – 67, 68 or 69?

32.   Up to the end of the 2007-08 season how many times has
       Bolton met Preston North End away – 70, 71 or 72?

33.   To the nearest five how many times has Bolton beaten Preston
       North End at home?

34.   To the nearest five how many times has Bolton beaten Preston
       North End away?

35.   What is the highest number of goals scored in a game
       between the two clubs?

36.   In season 1924-25 Bolton recorded their record score against
       Preston North End. What was the score of the First Division
       game played on 11 October 1924?

37.   Can you recall the season in which the two clubs last met in
       a competitive fixture?

38.   Bolton first met Preston North End in a competitive fixture in
       season 1885-86. What competition did they meet in?

39.   In season 1958-59 Bolton beat Preston North End 1-0 in an
       FA Cup 5th Round second replay. Can you name the
       Lancashire ground used as a neutral venue for the second
       replay?

40.   Bolton lost 2-1 away to Preston North End in this Cup
       competition in season 1991-92. Can you recall the name of
       the Cup?

MR CONSISTENCY - I

*All you have to do here is associate the player (and his appearances)
with the season in which he played the most games for the Trotters*

41.	Warren Joyce, 55	1994-95
42.	Gundi Bergsson, 51	1973-74
43.	Julian Darby, 56	1997-98
44.	Gary Speed, 42	1986-87
45.	Jimmy Phillips, 58	2003-04
46.	Alan Gowling, 45	1991-92
47.	Per Frandsen, 43	1959-60
48.	Barry Siddall, 50	2006-07
49.	Ivan Campo/Kevin Nolan, 44	1980-81
50.	Doug Holden, 45	2000-01

LEGEND – NAT LOFTHOUSE - 1

51.   In what year did Nat sign for Bolton Wanderers?

52.   In what year did Nat make his debut for the Trotters?

53.   How many goals did Nat score on his debut for Bolton?

54.   Against which London club did Nat make his First Division debut for the Trotters?

55.   To the nearest five how many full international caps did Nat win for England?

56.   In what year did he make his full international debut for England– 1948, 1949 or 1950?

57.   What is Nat's nickname?

58.   How did he obtain his nickname?

59.   In what year during the early 1950s was he named Footballer of the Year?

60.   To the nearest 50 how many league appearances did Nat make for Bolton?

BURNDEN PARK - I

61.   In what year did Bolton play their first game at Burnden Park
        – 1894, 1895 or 1896?

62.   What stand at Burnden Park featured in the 1962 film A Kind
        of Loving starring Alan Bates and June Ritchie?

63.   In what year during the 1940s did the Burnden Park Disaster
        occur?

64.   Why was a section of terracing at the ground sold off in 1986?

65.   Who was the Bolton player to score the last ever goal at
        Burnden Park?

66.   What were the Bolton players presented with shortly after
        their last ever competitive game at Burnden Park?

67.   In what year did Bolton play their last ever game at Burnden
        Park?

68.   This Athletic team was the last team Bolton played at Burnden
        Park in a competitive fixture. Name them.

69.   Can you name the famous Robert Burns song the fans sang at
        Burnden Park during the last ever game played at the ground?

70.   What supermarket company is now the principal tenant on
        the ground where Burnden Park once stood?

WINNERS – I

*All you have to do here is match the trophy with the
year Bolton Wanderers won it*

71.	Lancashire Cup	1929
72.	FA Cup	1909
73.	Football League War Cup North	1958
74.	Football League War Cup	1886
75.	Lancashire Cup	1958
76.	FA Charity Shield	1990
77.	FA Cup	1988
78.	Lancashire Cup	1945
79.	Football League Second Division	1923
80.	FA Cup	1945

BOLTON IN THE 1990s

81.   During what season in the early 1990s did Bolton Wanderers record a club record 23 League games without defeat?

82.   On 27 October 1990 the Trotters beat this "City" 1-0 at Burnden Park in Division Three. The win was Bolton's 1,000th home League victory. Name either the "City" or the "Tony" who scored.

83.   Can you name the Scottish striker Bolton obtained on loan in season 1991-92 and who scored within seconds of his introduction as substitute in a 2-2 draw at Exeter City in Division Three on 11 January 1992?

84.   On 8 May 1993 Bolton won their final Division Three game of the season 1-0 at Burnden Park which earned the Trotters promotion to Division 2. Can you name the Bolton goal scorer from the penalty spot?

85.   On 5 March 1994 Bolton beat Charlton Athletic 3-2 at Burnden Park in Division One. Can you name the Bolton Wanderers striker who scored a hat-trick in the game?

86.   In what season during the 1990s did Bolton Wanderers play at Wembley Stadium twice?

87.   When Bolton won promotion to the Premier League for season 1995-06, how many years had it been since the club last played top flight football?

88.   In August 1994 the Trotters purchased this Surinam-born striker from the Dutch side FC Volendam for what was a club record transfer fee at the time of £400,000. Who is he?

89.   On 17 May 1995 Peter Shilton became the oldest player ever to wear a Bolton shirt at 45 years 239 days of age when he played in the Trotters 2-1 play-off semi-final away loss. Who provided the opposition?

90.   What team did Bolton Wanderers defeat 4-3 after extra time at Wembley Stadium on 29 May 1995 in the Division One play-off Final?

BOLTON IN THE 1960s

91.   What is historically significant about Wanderers First Division game away to Blackpool on 10 September 1960, a game they won 1-0 to record their first away win of the 1960-61 season?

92.   Can you name the "City" Bolton drew 2-2 away with on 17 December 1960 in Division One, a game in which Nat Lofthouse sustained an injury which brought an end to his illustrious career?

93.   This "Dennis" was sold to Everton in March 1962 for a club record transfer fee at the time of £35,000. Name him.

94.   In season 1963-64 this young Bolton striker became the first Trotter to be capped at full international level by Wales in over 30 years. Who is he?

95.   In season 1965-66 Burnden Park hosted an FA Cup semi-final. Can you name either one of the two Lancashire sides involved in the game?

96.   On 3 February 1968 Bolton Wanderers beat Blackburn Rovers 2-1 at Burnden Park in the Second Division. What happened in the 85th minute of the game that had to be subsequently corrected by the referee to comply with the laws of the game?

97.   What did Bolton do during the summer of 1969-70 and retain throughout the 1969-70 and 1971-72 seasons?

98.   He entered season 1969-70 as his fourteenth as a Wanderer and on the opening day of the season made his 500th appearance for the club in the Trotters 4-1 win over Millwall at Burnden Park in Division Two. Name him.

99.   What happened at Burnden Park on 18 December 1968?

100.   This player joined the Trotters from Liverpool in December 1969 for a fee of £32,000 after originally deciding against a move to Burnden Park. Name him.

KEVIN NOLAN

101. In what year did Kevin sign youth academy forms for Bolton Wanderers having previously played as a schoolboy with his hometown club Liverpool?

102. How old was Kevin when he made his debut for the Trotters?

103. Kevin made his Wanderers debut against a London club. Name them.

104. In what year did Kevin sign professional forms with the Trotters?

105. Can you name the team with the letter "x" in their name that Kevin scored his first goal for the Trotters against?

106. Name the team Kevin scored against in the Premier League on 20 October 2001 in a game the Trotters won 2-1 away to record their first victory over this club in more than 20 years.

107. How many Premier League goals did Kevin score in season 2001-02 – 8, 9 or 10?

108. In what season was Kevin very close to winning a call-up to the England team for the first time?

109. What did Kevin do on 29 September 2005 that no other Trotter up to that point had ever done?

110. Mid-way through the 2005-06 season Kevin was appointed the club captain. Who did he succeed?

THREE LIONS ON A SHIRT

111.   Who is Bolton's most capped England international?

112.   Can you name the last Bolton player to be capped by England (up to the 31 December 2007)?

113.   What is the highest number of Bolton players to play in the same England team in a game?

114.   This Trotter with a money-sounding surname was first capped by England in 1958 and went on to win six caps. Name him.

115.   Can you name the Bolton player, who shares the same name as an ex-Everton player playing in the Scottish Premier League in season 2007-08, who in 1889 became the second Trotter to be capped by England?

116.   To the nearest five how many Bolton players have been capped by England at full international level?

117.   How many different Bolton players have scored for England in a full international?

118.   This Bolton striker scored on his England debut against Northern Ireland at Wembley on 18 November 1959 and remains the last Trotter to score for England in a full international. Name him.

119.   Can you name the Bolton goalkeeper who started five games for England alongside his team-mate Albert Holden, all in April and May 1959, against Scotland, Italy, Brazil, Peru and Mexico?

120.   This former Bolton manager won 43 caps for England and captained the national side 15 times. Can you name him?

THE HISTORY – 2

121. What was the occupation of Thomas Ogden, the founder of the club?

122. Can you name the club's first ever opponents, a street full of players, beginning with the letter "F"?

123. Who objected to club meetings being held in Christ Church School unless he was present – the Headmaster, the local MP or the Vicar?

124. This hotel in Bolton, sharing the same surname of the Liberal Party's British Prime Minister (1868–74, 1880–85, 1886 and 1892–94), was the location where the name Bolton Wanderers was first suggested. Name the hotel.

125. In what season during the 1880s did Bolton Wanderers enter the FA Cup for the first time?

126. Can you name the Lancashire side that Bolton Wanderers first lost to in an FA Cup tie?

127. Prior to moving to Burnden Park Bolton Wanderers played their home games at this fishy sounding Lane. Can you name the Lane?

128. What did the Bolton fans do to referee Sam Ormerod after a home game in 1883 that almost led to the club being expelled from the Lancashire FA?

129. Can you name any one of the three Cups Bolton won in season 1885-86?

130. In season 1890-91 Bolton Wanderers beat Darwen 3-1 in the final of the County Cup. Bolton won the game at Everton's ground but can you name it?

PLAYERS - I

131. Name the UEFA Champions League winner who arrived at the Reebok in the summer of 2002.

132. Can you name the Bolton Wanderers midfielder from the 2007-08 season who won representative honours at both Rugby Union and Cricket and has been capped by England at under-17 and under-18 levels?

133. What do Sam Ashton, Ralph Banks, Tommy Banks, Paul Fletcher, Roy Greaves, Paul Griffin, David Hatton, Nicky Hunt, Francis Lee, Nat Lofthouse, Roger Walker, Terry Wharton and Tom Woodward all have in common in the history of Bolton Wanderers?

134. Can you name the former Trotter who was forced to retire from the game when he suffered an injury playing for the MetroStars/RBNY in the 2nd leg of the MLS Eastern Conference semi-finals on 29 October 2006?

135. When Don McAllister joined Tottenham Hotspur for a fee of £80,000 in season 1974-75 can you name the teenager, and future Bolton Wanderers manager, who took his place in the team?

136. How many hat-tricks did Nat Lofthouse score for England?

137. This French-born Ivorian international player scored his first goal for Bolton Wanderers in their 3-1 FA Cup 4th Round replay defeat to Arsenal at the Reebok on 14 February 2007. Who is he?

138. Can you name the former Wanderers and Danish international midfielder who in 2007 was appointed assistant manager to former Trotters boss Colin Todd at the Danish Superliga side Randers FC?

139. In May 1971 Bolton Wanderers hosted a Testimonial Match for their long-serving goalkeeper Eddie Hopkinson. Can you name the famous Portuguese striker who was among the stars to play in the game at Burnden Park?

140. Who was the first player Sammy Lee signed for Bolton, putting pen to paper on a four year contract on 1 July 2007?

THE HISTORY – 3

141. How many goals did Nat Lofthouse score for Bolton in their opening nine league games of the 1956-57 season?

142. During the 1956-57 season this "Eddie" made his debut in goal for Bolton and went to on establish himself as a first team regular making a record number of league appearances for the Trotters. Name him.

143. What new facility did Burnden Park get in 1957-58?

144. What trophy did Bolton Wanderers win in October 1958 after defeating the reigning First Division Champions Wolverhampton Wanderers?

145. When Nat Lofthouse scored for England against the USSR in 1958 he equalled the record number of England goals (30) held by a Preston North End player. Can you name him?

146. What type of injury ultimately forced Nat Lofthouse to retire from playing football in season 1959-60?

147. In season 2007-08 Bolton Wanderers received the fewest red cards in the Premier League. How many Trotters players were sent off during the season?

148. To the nearest 500 what is Bolton's lowest ever recorded home attendance?

149. Bolton beat this Yorkshire club 8-0 at home in League game, the club's record league victory. Can you name their opponents?

150. Bolton beat this club, whose home kit has similar colours to Bolton's traditional colours, 6-1 at Burnden Park in a League Cup tie, the club's record home win in the competition. Name them.

FINAL APPEARANCES - I

*All you have to do here is match the Final to the year
the Trotters played in it*

151.	FA Cup Final	1990
152.	League Cup Final	1945
153.	FA Premier League Asia Trophy Final	1923
154.	Lancashire Cup Final	2004
155.	FA Cup Final	1988
156.	League Cup Final	1904
157.	Lancashire Cup Final	1894
158.	FA Cup Final	1995
159.	Football League War Cup Final	1925
160.	Lancashire Cup Final	2005

THE FOREIGN LEGION - I

161. This ex-Bolton Wanderers goalkeeper holds the distinction of being the first American goalkeeper to play in the Premier League when he played for Queens Park Rangers in 1995. Name him.

162. Who was the first Senegalese international to play for the Trotters?

163. Can you name the Icelandic player who joined Bolton Wanderers in 1997?

164. This Danish player arrived at the Reebok in 2000. Name him.

165. Can you name the Bolton manager who signed Mixu Paatelainen, Richard Sneekes and Fabian De Freitas?

166. This Italian arrived at the Reebok in 2000. Who is he?

167. John Gope-Fenepej signed for the Trotters in 2000. What nationality is he?

168. Can you name either the Dane or the Icelandic player who joined the Trotters in 1999?

169. Name the first player born in Guatemala to play for Bolton Wanderers.

170. Can you name the first South African player to sign for Bolton Wanderers?

MIXED BAG - 2

171. Who is the only man to have managed Bolton on two separate occasions?

172. Can you recall the name of the bank that adorned the Bolton kit in season 1982-83 as the club's official sponsor?

173. This "Joe" holds the record for the most number of hat-tricks scored for Bolton Wanderers with 10 to his name. Can you name him?

174. In terms of total medals won during his professional career who is the most successful player ever to have played for Bolton?

175. In what position did the Trotters finish in Division 1 in season 1999-2000 – 4th, 5th or 6th?

176. Can you name the Bolton "George" who won his only England cap in their 1-0 win over Holland on 18 May 1935 in Amsterdam?

177. This "Harold" (Wanderers 1926-32) holds the club record in terms of goals scored against appearances (minimum of 20 goals) with a goal every 122 minutes (122 goals in 165 appearances). Name him.

178. Can you name the "local" team Bolton Wanderers hammered 9-0 in an FA Cup 1st Round tie on 10 November 1883?

179. Bolton Wanderers won promotion from Division Three to Division Two at the end of the 1992-93 season with a new club record points total for a season? How many points did they win from their 46 League games?

180. Prior to Ivan Campo and Kevin Nolan sharing the honours in season 2003-04, who was the last player to end the season as the club's leading goal scorer and make the most appearances for the team during the season?

FORMER AWAY GROUNDS

181. If Bolton Wanderers had paid a visit to Maine Road in the past, what team would have been the home side?

182. If Bolton Wanderers had paid a visit to Filbert Street in the past, what team would have been the home side?

183. If Bolton Wanderers had paid a visit to Arsenal Stadium in the past, what team would have been the home side?

184. If Bolton Wanderers had paid a visit to Ayresome Park in the past, what team would have been the home side?

185. If Bolton Wanderers had paid a visit to Plough Lane in the past, what team would have been the home side?

186. If Bolton Wanderers had paid a visit to The Goldstone Ground in the past, what team would have been the home side?

187. If Bolton Wanderers had paid a visit to Highfield Road in the past, what team would have been the home side?

188. If Bolton Wanderers had paid a visit to The Dell in the past, what team would have been the home side?

189. If Bolton Wanderers had paid a visit to Elm Park in the past, what team would have been the home side?

190. If Bolton Wanderers had paid a visit to The Baseball Ground in the past, what team would have been the home side?

LEGEND - JAY-JAY OKOCHA - I

191. What is Jay-Jay's full name?

192. In what year did Jay-Jay sign for Bolton Wanderers?

193. What nationality is Jay-Jay?

194. Can you recall the club Jay-Jay played for prior to signing for Bolton?

195. Jay-Jay began his professional career with this German league side. Name them.

196. In 2002 Jay-Jay almost signed for this Lancashire club before they opted for David Ginola instead. Can you name the Premier League team?

197. Can you name the year in which Jay-Jay was first capped at full international level by his country?

198. Name the English league side Jay-Jay signed for on 4 September 2007.

199. To the nearest 25 how many appearances did Jay-Jay make for the Trotters?

200. Name the club Jay-Jay signed for when he left the Reebok Stadium.

GARY SPEED

201. At what club did Gary begin his professional career?

202. In what year did Gary sign for Bolton Wanderers?

203. Can you name the club Gary played for prior to signing for Bolton?

204. What did Gary win with the team in Q201 in season 1991-92?

205. Gary signed for this Premier League team in 1996. Name them.

206. On 9 December 2006 Gary played in Bolton Wanderers' 4-0 win over this "United" thereby becoming the first player to make 500 appearances in the Premier League. Can you name the United?

207. How much did the team in Q205 pay for Gary's services - £5.5m, £6.5m or £7.5m?

208. To the nearest 10 how many international appearances did Gary make for Wales?

209. In what year did Gary retire from international football?

210. On 24 December 2007 Gary agreed to join this Championship side. Name them.

THE HISTORY – 4

211. Prior to the start of the 1935-36 season renovation work was carried out to the Burnden and Great Lever Stands at Burnden Park. A local brewery, Magee's, supplied something which was incorporated into the roof of each stand and remained there for over 40 years. What did they supply?

212. How many times has Bolton Wanderers won the Lancashire Cup?

213. The players from Bolton Wanderers and a London club signed-up for War duties en masse after Britain declared War against Germany in September 1939. Can you name the London club?

214. On 21 October 1939 Bolton drew 1-1 at Burnley in a North West Regional League game. What strange colour kit did the Wanderers wear for the game (comprising of two colours)?

215. What did the Ministry of Supply store in the stands at Burden Park during World War II?

216. Can you recall the aptly named Bolton goalkeeper who got lost on his way to Bolton's game against Manchester United on 25 January 1941 resulting in the Wanderers having to start the game with just 10 men?

217. A Preston North End player, who went on to become a famous Liverpool manager, promised to play wartime football for Bolton Wanderers in season 1942-43 before his unit was transferred to Scotland. Name him.

218. What "united" did Bolton beat in the final of the League North Cup in season 1944-45?

219. Can you name Bolton's opponents in the final of the North versus South League Cup winners in June 1945?

220. How many league games had Bolton played in season 1939-40 before war with Germany was declared forcing regular league football to be scrapped?

THE BOSS – I

221. Can you name the former Bolton Wanderers manager from the 1990s who football legend Kenny Dalglish described in an interview as the best player he had ever played against?

222. This "Stan", a former Bolton Wanderers manager, played for Middlesbrough, Newcastle United and Sunderland and became the first player to captain all three of the big north east clubs. Who is he?

223. In season 1998-99 this former Trotters boss guided Cambridge United to promotion to Division Two after finishing runners-up in Division Three. Who is he?

224. At what club did former Trotters boss Sammy Lee begin his professional playing career?

225. What Cup did Walter Rowley (Wanderers manager 1944-50) guide the Trotters to success in season 1944-45?

226. This Bolton Wanderers manager from the 1970s began his professional career as a player with Manchester United in 1953 and won a First Division Championship winners' medal and an FA Cup runners-up medal with the Red Devils at full-back. Who is he?

227. Can you name the former Wanderers manager from the early 1970s who played for Blackpool throughout his entire professional career?

228. This legendary Bolton Wanderers player (1908-27, 492 league appearances and 277 league goals for the Trotters) was the manager of Blackpool when they beat Wanderers in the 1953 FA Cup Final. Who is he?

229. George Mulhall was in charge of Bolton Wanderers for one year during the 1980s before rumours circulated that he was to be replaced by a former Brazilian international. Can you name the Brazilian master?

230. At the age of 19 this future Trotters boss became the youngest player to play in all four divisions of the Football League. Name him.

231. Can you recall who scored Bolton's opening goal of the 2006-07 season in a 2-0 Premier League win over Tottenham Hotspur at the Reebok?

232. This London club was the first to beat Bolton in the Premier League during the season. Name them.

233. Can you name the West Midlands team Bolton beat 3-1 away in the League Cup 2nd Round and who went on to win League Two in season 2006-07?

234. On 20 September 2006 Bolton beat Liverpool 2-0 in the Premier League at the Reebok. Name any Trotter goal scorer.

235. Bolton lost their first home game of the season on 28 October 2006. What club hammered them 4-0?

236. Bolton beat Arsenal 3-1 at the Reebok in the Premier League on 25 November 2006. Nicolas Anelka scored twice but who else was on the score sheet for the Trotters?

237. Thee days after the Arsenal win in Q236 the Trotters welcomed another London club to the Reebok. Who beat them 1-0?

238. Bolton lost 3-0 away to this Lancashire club in the Premier League on New Year's Day. Name them.

239. This London side knocked the Trotters out of the FA Cup in a 4th Round replay. Can you name them?

240. Name the club the Trotters beat 3-2 at the Reebok in their final game of 2006 thanks to goals from Abdoulaye Faye, Ivan Campo and Nicolas Anelka.

MIXED BAG – 3

241. Between 1992 and 1999 Bolton had three managers who all won a First Division League Championship winners' medal in season 1974-75. Name the club they played for.

242. Can you name the Trotter who played in all Denmark's matches at the 2002 FIFA World Cup Finals and who played his last game for his country in the 3-0 defeat to England in the first knock-out round?

243. In what position did the Trotters finish in Division 1 in season 2000-01 – 3rd, 4th or 5th?

244. Which Bolton player has scored the most number of goals for England?

245. Can you name the former Bolton legend who began his football career with Enugu Rangers in Africa?

246. Bolton beat this Yorkshire "United" 13-0 at home in an FA Cup tie on 1 February 1890, the club's record score in the competition. Can you name their opponents?

247. This "Albert" (Wanderers 1904-09) is ranked second in the club record books for the record number of goals scored against appearances (minimum of 20 goals) with a goal every 123 minutes (90 goals in 123 appearances). Name him.

248. Can you name the player (he played one full game and made one substitute appearance for Bolton Wanderers) who in 1997 played his 1,000th league game before retiring from the game aged 47 after 1,005 league appearances?

249. What vacant manager's job was Bolton's Gary Speed linked to in 2004?

250. Of the 43 games the Trotters actually played during the 2006-07 season, how many did they lose – 16, 17 or 18?

MR CONSISTENCY - 2

All you have to do here is associate the player (and his appearances)
with the season in which he played the most games for the Trotters

251.	Michael Johansen, 61	1993-94
252.	Charlie Wright, 56	1996-97
253.	Jason McAteer, 62	2002-03
254.	David Felgate, 59	2005-06
255.	Jossi Jaaskelainen, 38	1963-64
256.	Chris Fairclough, 54	1957-58
257.	Simon Farnworth, 57	1999-2000
258.	Roy Hartle, 45	1990-91
259.	Tal Ben Haim, 49	1971-72
260.	John Higgins, 49	1984-85

THE HISTORY – 5

261. What type of certificates did the Bolton players receive after beating Chelsea in the 1945 north versus south League Cup winners final?

262. In what season during World War II did Bill Shankly make guest appearances for Bolton Wanderers?

263. This "Ray" left Bolton at the end of the 1947-48 season after 18 years' loyal service to the Trotters. Can you name him?

264. In season 1949-50 Bolton paid a club record transfer fee of £20,000 to bring this "Bobby" to Burnden Park from Preston North End. Can you name the winger?

265. On the opening day of the 1950-51 season Nat Lofthouse scored a hat-trick in a 4-3 away defeat to this "Athletic" club. Name them.

266. Can you name Bolton's secretary/manager who handed in his resignation on 17 October 1950 after having spent 39 years with the Trotters?

267. In season 1951-52 Bolton appointed this "Bill" to the coaching staff at Burnden Park. Can you name the former Leeds United, Tottenham Hotspur, Manchester City and England full back?

268. In season 1951-52 this "Ray" became the club's youngest ever League debutant aged just 15 years and 267 days. Can you name him?

269. Nat Lofthouse captained Bolton Wanderers for the first time during season 1955-56. Can you name the "Town" who provided Bolton's FA Cup 3rd Round opponents?

270. What caused the game in Q189 to be abandoned after 47 minutes with the score at 0-0?

BIG SAM ALLARDYCE – I

271. Can you name the League of Ireland side that gave Big Sam his first taste of management in season 1991-92?

272. To what Midlands club was Big Sam named as assistant manager (player-coach) to Brian Talbot in February 1989?

273. Name the London club Big Sam signed for when he left Sunderland in 1981.

274. To the nearest 25 how many league appearances did Big Sam make for the Trotters?

275. Can you recall the name of the Florida-based North American Soccer League side Big Sam played for in the summer of 1983?

276. Big Sam managed this seaside club from 1994-96. Name them.

277. What "City" did Big Sam play for in season 1983-84?

278. Can you recall the Lancashire club, and historically bitter rival, Big Sam joined when he left the Trotters for a second time in 1986?

279. On 19 September 2006 Big Sam and his son Craig were implicated in a BBC documentary for taking "bungs" from agents for signing certain players. Name the BBC TV show.

280. Can you name the famous English Music Festival Big Sam paid £10,500 to purchase the first tickets for at a charity auction in 2007?

THE HISTORY – 6

281.　At the end of the 1890-91 season Bolton was admitted to a Lancashire-based Football Association. Can you name the Association which also bears the name of a city?

282.　In season 1893-94 Bolton Wanderers reached the FA Cup Final for the first time. Who were their opponents?

283.　At what ground was the 1894 FA Cup Final played – Anfield, Ewood Park or Goodison Park?

284.　What was significant about Bolton losing the first FA Cup Final they ever appeared in?

285.　In 1895 Burnden Park staged its first ever game. Can you name their opponents who wore a similar kit to Bolton's traditional kit?

286.　This Merseyside club provided Bolton's first ever opponents in a league game at Burnden Park. Name them.

287.　In what season during the late 1890s was Bolton relegated to Division Two for the first time in the club's history?

288.　Bolton won promotion to Division One at the end of the 1899-1900 season. Can you name the Yorkshire club they finished runners-up to?

289.　In 1901-02 Harold Williams scored twice for Bolton on his home debut against Newcastle United. Why did the FA Ban him from playing in Bolton's next league game away to Aston Villa?

290.　Following on from Q289 how many guineas was Bolton Wanderers fined over the incident?

NATIONALITIES

*All you have to do here is match the Bolton Wanderers
player from season 2007-08 to his nationality*

291.	Hunt, Nicky	Norway
292.	Anelka, Nicolas	USA
293.	Giannakopoulos, Stelios	Senegal
294.	Kazimierczak, Przemysław	Sweden
295.	O'Brien, Andy	France
296.	Wilhelmsson, Christian	Hungary
297.	Diouf, El Hadji	England
298.	Smith, Johann	Republic of Ireland
299.	Braaten, Daniel	Greece
300.	Bogdan, Adam	Poland

SHERPA VAN TROPHY
WINNERS 1988-89

301. Can you name either one of the two Lancashire teams the Trotters played in their two preliminary qualifying Group 1 games in the competition?

302. Name the Lancashire team Bolton beat 1-0 away in their 1st Round north fixture.

303. Bolton disposed of this Welsh side in their Area quarter-final tie of the competition. Name the team.

304. What was the score after extra time of the game in Q303?

305. This "Mark" scored twice against the team in Q303. Name him.

306. Name the team with the letter "x" in their name that Bolton defeated 2-1 away in their area semi-final.

307. Can you recall the seaside team Bolton met in their Area final?

308. What was the score over two legs of the Area final?

309. Bolton beat this "United", the Southern Area final winners, 4-1 in the final. Can you name them?

310. This stadium hosted the final. Can you recall where it was played?

FRANK WORTHINGTON - 1

311. In what year did Frank Worthington sign for Bolton Wanderers?

312. Can you recall the club Frank Worthington played for prior to signing for Bolton?

313. Frank Worthington began his professional career at this "Town". Name them.

314. Against what "City" did Frank Worthington make his league debut for the Trotters, scoring in a 1-1 draw at Burnden Park?

315. Can you name the year in which Frank Worthington was first capped at full international level by England?

316. To the nearest 20 how many league appearances did Frank Worthington make for the Trotters?

317. In what year did Frank leave Bolton Wanderers – 1979, 1980 or 1981?

318. Name the "City" Frank Worthington signed for when he left Burnden Park.

319. How many full international caps did Frank Worthington win for England – 8, 9 or 10?

320. To the nearest 10 how many League goals did Frank Worthington score for the Trotters?

BOLTON WANDERERS
v BURNLEY

321. Up to the end of the 2007-08 season how many times has Bolton met Burnley at home – 57, 58 or 59?

322. Up to the end of the 2007-08 season how many times has Bolton met Burnley away – 58, 59 or 60?

323. To the nearest five how many times has Bolton beaten Burnley at home?

324. To the nearest five how many times has Bolton beaten Burnley away?

325. What is the highest number of goals scored in a game between the two clubs?

326. In season 1934-35 Bolton recorded their record score against Burnley. What was the score of the First Division game played on 2 January 1935?

327. Can you recall the season in which the two clubs last met in a competitive fixture?

328. Bolton first met Burnley in a competitive fixture in season 1888-89. What competition did they meet in?

329. This "Joe" holds the Bolton Wanderers record for most number of career goals scored for the Trotters against Burnley with 11. Name him.

330. Bolton lost 2-1 away to Burnley in this Cup competition in season 1983-84. Can you recall the name of the Cup?

SEASON 2005-06 - 1

331. Can you recall the striker who scored Bolton's opening goal of the 2005-06 season in a 2-2 Premier League away draw with Aston Villa?

332. This Lancashire club was the first to beat Bolton in the Premier League during the season. Name the team that defeated the Trotters in their first home game of the season.

333. Can you name the London club Bolton beat 1-0 at home in the League Cup 3rd Round?

334. On 3 December 2005 Bolton beat Arsenal 2-0 in the Premier League at the Reebok. Name any Trotter goal scorer.

335. Bolton lost their first Premier League away game of the season on 2 October 2005. What "Athletic" club beat them 2-1?

336. What London club did Bolton beat 1-0 at the Reebok in the 4th Round of the FA Cup on 28 January 2006?

337. Two weeks after the game in Q336 the Trotters visited the same club in the Premier League and drew 1-1. Who scored for Bolton?

338. Bolton drew 2-2 at the Reebok with this Lancashire club in the Premier League on 2 January 2006. Name them.

339. This London side knocked the Trotters out of the FA Cup in a 5th Round replay after extra time. Can you name them?

340. The Trotters beat Birmingham City 1-0 at the Reebok in their final game of the season. Can you name the player who scored his second goal in consecutive games for the Trotters?

341. In what year during the early 1970s did Sam Allardyce begin his professional football career with his first club, Bolton Wanderers?

342. What was the only honour Big Sam ever won as a player?

343. In what year during the early 1980s did Big Sam leave the Trotters as a player?

344. Name the north east club he signed for when he left Burnden Park.

345. Can you recall the Yorkshire club Big Sam joined when he left Burnden Park for a second time?

346. Big Sam played for this League of Ireland side in season 1991-92. Name them.

347. At what Lancashire club did Big Sam end his playing career?

348. Big Sam was born in Dudley, West Midlands. What famous Midlands club did he support as a boy?

349. Can you recall the year during the mid-1980s in which Big Sam re-signed for the Trotters?

350. In what year was Big Sam appointed the manager of Bolton Wanderers?

351. Prior to becoming the manager of Bolton Wanderers in 1915 Tom Mather was the Assistant Secretary of this Lancashire "City". Name them.

352. Who did Nat Lofthouse succeed as manager of Bolton Wanderers when Nat took charge of the club for the first time?

353. Name the Trotters manager who guided the club to three FA Cup wins.

354. This "Walter" had the unenviable task of taking charge of Bolton Wanderers after the man in Q353 stepped down. Name him.

355. Can you name the former Bolton Wanderers manager who played for both Manchester United and Manchester City during the 1930s?

356. Can you name the former Bolton Wanderers manager from the early 1970s who won 55 caps for Northern Ireland and scored 10 international goals for his country?

357. This former Bolton Wanderers manager played for Derby County, Sunderland, Everton, Birmingham City, Nottingham Forest, Oxford United, Vancouver Whitecaps and Luton Town and won 27 England caps. Name him.

358. At what south coast club did Gary Megson begin his professional career as a footballer?

359. Can you name the club that begins and ends with the same letter, that Charlie Wright (Wanderers manager 1984-85) managed from 1977-80?

360. In February 1989 Sam Allardyce was named as assistant manager (player-coach) to this man at West Bromwich Albion. The Albion manager won an FA Cup winners' medal with Ipswich Town in 1978 and again the following year with Arsenal. Who is he?

PLAYERS – 2

361. Apart from Gary Speed who is the only other player to have played in every Premier League season (1992-93 to 2007-08) and score in every season?

362. Nat Lofthouse scored four times for Bolton against this "City" in a 6-0 Division One win at Burnden Park on 10 December 1955. Name the City.

363. Can you name the Bolton midfielder who head-butted the owner of "Café Ketchup" in Copenhagen during the summer of 2002 and who was convicted to four months in jail, which he served from April to July 2003?.

364. Name the "Scott" who was allocated the No.46 shirt for the Trotters during the 2007-08 season.

365. Name the Bolton player who scored twice for the Trotters against Manchester United at Old Trafford in a memorable 2-1 First Division win on 11 April 1979, completing the double over the Red Devils after Bolton had won at home 3-0 earlier in the season.

366. Can you name the Trotter who scored the goal which secured a 2–2 draw for his country in his country's opening game of the 2006 FIFA World Cup Finals against Saudi Arabia?

367. Who was the last player to have been capped in goal by England and later went on to play for Bolton Wanderers during his career?

368. At the start of the 2007-08 season Bolton Wanderers obtained Jlloyd Samuel from Aston Villa. To the nearest £500,000 how much did he cost the Trotters?

369. This "Jack" (Wanderers 1929-38) is ranked fifth in the club record books for the record number of goals scored against appearances (minimum of 20 goals) with a goal every 150 minutes (153 goals in 255 appearances). Name him.

370. This former Trotter managed Manchester City, Sunderland, Leeds United and Coventry City. Who is he?

FA CUP RUNNERS-UP 1952-53

371.   Who was the Bolton Wanderers manager that guided the Trotters to Wembley?

372.   Can you name the Lancashire side that beat Bolton Wanderers in the Final?

373.   An opposing player won his first and only FA Cup Final winners' medal and the 1953 FA Cup Final was named after him. Who is he?

374.   Can you name the London club Bolton Wanderers beat 3-1 at Burnden Park in the 3rd Round?

375.   It took Bolton three games, two replays, to see off this "County" in the 4th Round. Name them.

376.   Nat Lofthouse scored the only goal of the game in this 5th Round 1-0 away win over this "Town". Can you name the Trotters' opponents?

377.   The Trotters faced and beat this north east club 1-0 in the quarter-finals at their Redheugh Park home in front of 17,692 fans. The home side, a non-league team, changed from their regular all white shirts to unfamiliar black and white stripes allowing the Trotters to wear the traditional colours for the game. Name them.

378.   Can you recall the team Bolton Wanderers beat 4-3 in the semi-finals?

379.   What ground hosted the game in Q378 – Hillsborough, Maine Road or Villa Park?

380.   What was the score in the Final?

MIXED BAG – 4

381.   Can you name the club Sam Allardyce managed from 1997-99?

382.   The Trotters purchased this Danish international prior to the 2001-02 season. Name him.

383.   This former Trotters boss managed Cambridge United, Torquay United and Chesterfield after he left Bolton Wanderers. Name him.

384.   In what Round of the FA Cup did Bolton meet Manchester United in season 1961-62?

385.   Can you name the "Robert" who was allocated the No.38 shirt for the Trotters during the 2007-08 season?

386.   To the nearest 15 minutes what is John McGinlay's scoring ratio for Wanderers in 245 games (15 as substitute) for the club, i.e. how many minutes it took him on average to score a goal?

387.   How many hat-tricks did Nat Lofthouse score for Bolton Wanderers?

388.   In what position did the Trotters finish in the Premier League in season 2001-02 – 16th, 17th or 18th?

389.   In what year did Reebok take over as the club's official shirt sponsor?

390.   Can you name the former Bolton manager who managed Coventry City from 1993-95?

DIVISION 2 CHAMPIONS
– 1908-09

391. Can you recall the club who became the first club to do the "Double" in the 20th century that finished runners-up to Bolton Wanderers in season 1908-09?

392. This "Billy" was the Trotters leading goal scorer with 16 league goals. Name him.

393. This Lancashire team finished bottom of the table but would go in to defeat Bolton Wanderers in an FA Cup Final. Name them.

394. In the final game of the season the Trotters beat this Midlands club 1-0 at Burnden Park. Can you name the team that would go on to win two First Division Championships during the 1970s?

395. How many of their 38 league games did the Trotters win – 24, 25 or 26?

396. Bolton lost their opening game of the season 2-0 to this "City", a Premier League club in season 2007-08. Name them.

397. The Trotters hammered this "County" 4-1 at Burnden Park in their penultimate home game of the season. Can you name their opponents?

398. Can you name either one of the two teams with three words to their name the Trotters met in the league during the season?

399. The Trotters beat this Yorkshire "City" 2-0 on Christmas Day at Burnden Park and 2-1 away the following day. Name the team that subsequently folded in 1919 only to be re-formed with a change of name to "United".

400. This "David" scored his only goal of the season in the 2-1 Boxing Day win in Q399 and shares the same surname with the player who scored the winning goal in the 1976 FA Cup Final. Name him.

FREIGHT ROVER TROPHY
RUNNERS-UP 1985-86

401. Can you name any one of the two teams that were in Group 2 North with Bolton?

402. What "Rovers" did the Trotters beat in their North Area quarter-final?

403. Bolton beat this team 3-0 away in their North Area semi-final. Can you name them?

404. Name either one of the two Bolton players who scored in both the quarter-finals and semi-finals.

405. Can you recall Bolton's North Area final opponents?

406. Following on from Q405, what was the score over the two legs in the North Area final?

407. What "City" beat Bolton in the Final?

408. Can you recall the score in the Final?

409. This London ground hosted the Final. Name it.

410. Apart from the two players in Q404, who else scored for Bolton in their Area semi-final win?

ASA HARTFORD

411. In what year during the mid-1980s did Asa Hartford join Bolton Wanderers?

412. From what "City" did the Trotters purchase Asa Hartford?

413. In what Division were Bolton Wanderers when Asa Hartford arrived at Burnden Park?

414. Can you name the "United" he made his Bolton Wanderers debut against?

415. Name the "County" he scored his first goal for Bolton against?

416. Following on from Q415, in what competition did he find the net?

417. To the nearest 20 how many games did Asa play for the Trotters in all competitions?

418. In what year did Asa leave Burnden Park?

419. Can you recall the "County" he signed for when he left Bolton Wanderers?

420. In 1976 Asa won a League Cup winners' medal in what remains this club's last ever trophy success. Name the team.

MIXED BAG – 5

421. This ex-Trotter was the first Tunisian to play in the Premier League. Name him.

422. What did Bolton Wanderers become the first Premier League club to do when they issued a Press Statement on 10 February 2007?

423. At the end of what season during the 1980s did the Trotters get relegated to Division Four for the first time in the club's history?

424. Can you name the former Trotters boss who concluded his coaching career with a brief spell as Assistant Manager at Peterborough United during the 1997-98 season?

425. In what position did the Trotters finish in the Premier League in season 2002-03 – 16th, 17th or 18th?

426. This "Malcolm", a Bolton centre half, played alongside Nat Lofthouse for England three times in internationals against Wales (October 1951), Northern Ireland (November 1951) and Scotland in April 1953. Name him.

427. At the start of the 2007-08 season Bolton Wanderers purchased Gavin McCann from Aston Villa. To the nearest £250,000 how much did he cost the Trotters?

428. Can you name the former Bolton Wanderers manager who was once the manager of the oldest English Football League club?

429. Name the two men who managed both Bolton Wanderers and Derby County.

430. How many international goals did Frank Worthington score for England– 1, 2, or 3?

2007-08 PRE-SEASON FRIENDLIES

431.   Can you name the Scottish club the Trotters lost 3-0 away to on 25 July 2007?

432.   Wanderers beat these "Rovers" 1-0 away on 28 July 2007. Name them.

433.   Name the Spanish visitors who lost 3-0 at the Reebok on 1 August 2007.

434.   He scored for Bolton Wanderers in the games in Q432 and 433. Name him.

435.   Bolton travelled to this "United" on 4 August 2007 and won 2-1 thanks to goals from Gary Speed (pen) and Ricardo Vaz-Te. Name them.

436.   Can you name Bolton's first opponents in the 2007 Peace Cup?

437.   On 14 July 2007 the Trotters beat Club Deportivo Guadalajara in the 2007 Peace Cup. Name either one of Bolton's two goal scorers.

438.   Name the Spanish club Bolton Wanderers beat 2-1 in the 2007 Peace Cup on 17 July 2007.

439.   This Bolton striker scored both goals for the Trotters in the game in Q438. Name him.

440.   The Trotters lost 1-0 to the French League Champions on 21 July 2007 in the Peace Cup Final. Name the winners of the 2007 Peace Cup.

THE FOREIGN LEGION - 2

441. Who in February 1979 became the first foreign player to sign for Bolton Wanderers?

442. Can you name the Yugoslavian midfielder the Trotters bought from Red Star Belgrade in 1980?

443. Bolton Wanderers signed this German international during the 2001-02 season. Who is he?

444. Name either one of the two Dutch players that signed for the Trotters after the 1994 FIFA World Cup Finals in the USA.

445. Kenneth Grieves played in goal for Bolton Wanderers during the 1950s and although considered to be a Lancastrian he was not actually born England. In what country was he born?

446. Can you name either the Icelandic player or Yugoslavian player who joined the Trotters in 1995?

447. Name either one of the two Danish players who arrived at Burnden Park in 1996.

448. What nationality was former Trotter Gaetano Giallanza?

449. This Frenchman joined the Trotters in 1999. Who is he?

450. Can you name the Australian who arrived at the Reebok in 2000?

BETWEEN THE STICKS

451. Can you name the Bolton Wanderers goalkeeper who scored for the Trotters in a 3-1 Division 2 league game against Burnley at Burnden Park on 15 January 1983?

452. On 28 August 2000 Jussi Jaaskelainen got injured in a 1-0 away win over Tranmere Rovers and missed the rest of the season. Can you name the reserve goalkeeper who took over in goal for the rest of the 2000-01 season?

453. In season 1991-92 Bolton used four different goalkeepers. Name any two of the four.

454. This on-loan veteran goalkeeper had a brief spell in nets for the Trotters in season 2000-01 but was refused permission by his club, Manchester City, to play in the 2000-01 FA Cup. Who is he?

455. During the 2000-01 season the Trotters suffered a goalkeeping crisis. Can you name the goalkeeper they pur chased from Revolution to help them through part of the season?

456. In late 1993 Bolton Wanderers had a mini goalkeeping crisis which resulted in them drafting in this goalkeeper on loan from Leicester City. Name him.

457. This Welsh B international was taken on loan by the Trotters from Manchester City during the 1993-94 season. Who is he?

458. Can you recall the name of the journeyman goalkeeper Bolton manager Bruce Rioch brought to Burnden Park to help ease a goalkeeping crisis the club had in season 1993-94?

459. On 6 November 1993 the Trotters drew 2-2 in the Championship away to West Bromwich Albion. Can you name the Bolton Wanderers goalkeeper who was sent off in game?

460. Name the "United" Jussi Jaaskelainen was sent off in a Premier League clash with in season 2001-02.

PLAYERS – 3

461. Can you name either one of the two players who made their debut for Bolton Wanderers in a 1-0 Worthington Cup defeat against local rivals Bury on 2 October 2002 and who never played for the first team again?

462. How many players have scored 100 or more League goals for Bolton Wanderers – 8, 9 or 10?

463. At the start of the 2007-08 season Bolton Wanderers purchased Andy O'Brien from Portsmouth. To the nearest £250,000 how much did he cost the Trotters?

464. Can you name the Bolton midfielder (2001-02) who is one of the few current footballers (Gillingham 2007-08) to have played in every division of English league football having started his career at Hartlepool United in League Two?

465. What reason did Dietmar Hamann give for leaving Bolton in the summer of 2006 just a few weeks after signing for the club?

466. Prior to Nicolas Anelka's £15m transfer to Chelsea on 11 January 2008, can you name the player who previously held the transfer record at Bolton Wanderers for a fee received by the Trotters?

467. Can you name the "Gordon" who on 9 October 1965 became the first ever Bolton substitute to be used when he came on for the injured John Napier during a 3-2 home defeat by Southampton?

468. What have Gareth Farrelly, Paul Fletcher, Per Frandsen, Francis Lee, Akinori Nishizawa, Michael Ricketts, Stuart Ripley, Andy Walker, Rod Wallace and Frank Worthington all got in common for Bolton Wanderers?

469. Sam Allardyce tried to sign this Birmingham City midfielder in January 2007 before the player later opted to rejoin his former club. Who is he?

470. This member of the 1994-95 play-off winning team starred alongside former Wanderers loanee Ally Maxwell in the 2000 movie A Shot at Glory starring Ally McCoist. Who is he?

THE BOSS – 3

471. Can you name the ex-Bolton boss who during the early 1980s appeared in an episode of Boys from the Blackstuff on BBC TV?

472. Name the Lancashire side Gary Megson joined in 1979 after he left Plymouth Argyle.

473. Charlie Wright managed Bolton Wanderers in season 1984-85. Who replaced him as manager of the Trotters in 1985?

474. This Bolton Wanderers manager guided the club to Division One play-off final success in season 1994-95 but this was his last game in charge of the Trotters. Who is he?

475. Can you name the "Rovers" that Bill Ridding (Wanderers manager 1950-68) managed from 1939-45?

476. Which player who went on to win a World Cup winners' medal with England in 1966, had a trial at the Trotters in 1961 but was rejected by manager Bill Ridding on the grounds that at 5 ft 6 ins he was too small to make the grade as a professional footballer?

477. This former Trotters boss began his professional playing career at Tranmere Rovers in 1966 and went on to play for Derby County, Bradford City and England. Who is he?

478. Can you name the "Town" Colin Todd managed after he left his post as manager of Bolton Wanderers?

479. This former Bolton Wanderers manager joined Sunderland in September 1962 for £25,000 and went on to make 253 league appearances 966 league goals) for the club where he still holds the record for the most consecutive appearances, 125. Can you name him?

480. This ex-Bolton manager from the 1970s was awarded an OBE in 2000 and appointed a Deputy Lieutenant of his home county of Lancashire in 2004. In 2005–06 he served as High Sheriff of Lancashire. Name him.

MIXED BAG – 6

481. Can you name the brothers who became the first set of twins to play for the club?

482. Can you recall what was installed at the Reebok Stadium in time for the 2007-2008 season, an item used by many other leading clubs such as Manchester United and Real Madrid?

483. Name the manager who steered Bolton out of the Fourth Division in season 1987-88.

484. In what position did the Trotters finish in the Premier League in season 2005-06 – 8th, 9th or 10th?

485. What have Sam Ashton, Dennis Bailey, Wayne Buchanan, Paul Griffin, Mickael Kapriellian, Craig Moores, Andy Oakes, Lee Potter, Dean Roberts, John Simm, Juergen Sommer, Luke Staton and Jani Viander all got in common for Bolton Wanderers?

486. In season 2000-01 season Bolton Wanderers suffered a goal keeping crisis. Can you recall the name of the goalkeeper who joined the club shortly before the transfer deadline from Bradford City?

487. Can you name either one of the two Bolton first team players who took charge of the Wanderers reserve team for the game against Manchester United on 20 January 2005 because their coach Neil McDonald was unavailable?

488. In what year were Mick Channon and John Wile both linked with the vacant manager's job at Bolton Wanderers?

489. Name any three Bolton Wanderers players who left the club for a fee of £4m or more.

490. Can you name the legendary singer who Lofty the Lion does impressions of before home games?

MAIDEN EUROPEAN ADVENTURE

491. Why did Bolton Wanderers success in the 1958 FA Cup Final not earn them a place in Europe the following season?

492. In what season did Bolton Wanderers first play in one of the three major European club football competitions?

493. Following on from Q492, can you name Bolton's first ever European opponents?

494. What country is the team in Q493 from?

495. Can you recall the score of the game in Q493 that was played at the Reebok?

496. Who scored Bolton's first ever European goal?

497. Two weeks after the game in Q493 the return leg was played. Who scored Bolton's first ever away goal in European competition?

498. Name any of the four teams Bolton met in the Group Stage of the competition in their maiden European campaign.

499. What round of the competition did the Trotters reach in their maiden European campaign?

500. Can you recall the French side that knocked Bolton out of Europe and also became the first team to defeat the Trotters in a European competition?.

NAMED AND NUMBERED

501. In what season did Bolton Wanderers first introduce squad numbers?

502. Following on from Q501, who wore the No.1 jersey that season?

503. In the season mentioned in Q501 two players actually wore the No.4 jersey for the Trotters during the season. Name either of them.

504. Two players named John wore the No.10 shirt during the 1997-98 season. Name both of them.

505. Can you name the "Kevin" who was allocated the No.44 shirt for the Trotters during the 2007-08 season?

506. Who was handed the No.1 jersey to wear for the 2000-01 season?

507. Can you recall the shirt number Jussi Jaaskelainen was handed when he first arrived at the Reebok?

508. In season 2000-01 Bo Hansen was handed the No.9 shirt having worn No.14 the previous season. Can you name the striker who vacated the No.9 shirt at the end of the 1999-2000 season?

509. What shirt number did Les Ferdinand wear for the Trotters in his only season with the club, 2004-05?

510. In season 2002-03 Jay-Jay Okocha was given the No.10 shirt to wear. Who wore No.10 for the Trotters over the previous three seasons?

PLAYERS - 4

511. Can you name Ivan Campo's Real Madrid team-mate, a former England international, who persuaded him to move to the Premier League and to Bolton Wanderers?

512. Name either one of the two teams that Youri Djorkaeff won the European Cup Winners' Cup with in season 1995-96 or the UEFA Cup with in season 1997-98?

513. To the nearest 10 how many full international caps did Jay-Jay Okocha win playing for Nigeria?

514. Can you name either one of the two "Buchan" brothers who became the second pair of brothers to play for the club when they played in the same Bolton Wanderers team during World War 1?

515. On how many occasions did Nat Lofthouse score two goals in a game for England – 10, 11 or 12?

516. This former Bolton Wanderers Danish international won the Danish Cup three times, in 1992, 1996 and 2006. Name him.

517. Can you name the club Kevin Davies reached the semi-finals of the FA Cup with in 1997 only to lose to Middlesbrough?

518. When he left the Reebok Stadium Jermaine Johnson signed for this "Athletic" club. Name them.

519. This Bolton Wanderers player became the first Arab footballer to sign for a Premier League team when he arrived at the Reebok in January 2006. Who is he?

520. From what club did Bolton Wanderers sign Heidar Helguson in July 2007?

KEVIN DAVIES

521.   In what year did Kevin Davies join Bolton Wanderers?

522.   Name the club the Trotters obtained Kevin Davies from in a free transfer.

523.   Can you name the club where Kevin began his professional career?

524.   Kevin made his Wanderers Premier League debut against this "United" Name them.

525.   Name the team Kevin moved to on 2 June 1998.

526.   Following on from Q525, to the nearest £1.25m how much did Kevin cost this team?

527.   Kevin's first goal for Bolton Wanderers came against one of his former clubs. Name them.

528.   What London club was Kevin on loan to for a while in 2003?

529.   Can you name the club Kevin has had two different spells with?

530.   What two runners-up' medals has Kevin won?

IVAN CAMPO

531. In what year did Ivan Campo first join Bolton Wanderers on loan?

532. Name the club the Trotters signed Ivan Campo from in a free transfer.

533. Can you name the "Deportivo" in Spain where Ivan Campo began his professional career?

534. Ivan made his Wanderers Premier League debut against a Lancashire club. Name them.

535. Name the Primera Liga "Real" that Ivan was loaned to in 1995-96.

536. Following on from Q535, can you name the Spanish club that plays their home games at the Mestalla that loaned Ivan to this team?

537. Ivan's first goal for Bolton Wanderers came against this Lancashire club. Name them.

538. What "Real" was Ivan loaned to for the 1997-98 season?

539. By what affectionate nickname is Ivan known by in Spain?

540. Can you name the position Ivan played in when he began his career with the team in Q531?

541. In season 2007-08 this Bolton Wanderers player was noted for being the only Christian footballer in his national team. Name him.

542. What does Heidar Helguson's surname mean when it is translated to English from Icelandic?

543. This Bolton Wanderers player from season 2007-08 played junior football for YMCA juniors in Lytham St Annes and both his father and grandfather are huge Wanderers fans having been born and bred in Bolton. Who is he?

544. Name the winger Bolton signed on 3 August 2007 whose two previous clubs were Skeid (2000-04) and Rosenborg Ballklub (2004-07).

545. Name the player the Trotters purchased in January 2007 but then loaned out to Leeds United before recalling him back to the Reebok before the season ended.

546. On 17 May 2007 Sammy Lee signed this 19-year old striker on a three year permanent deal after a successful spell in the reserves netting three goals in seven games during a loan spell. Who is he?

547. This Bolton Wanderers midfielder from the 2007-08 season made his first team debut for the Trotters in the 3rd Round of the 2005-06 FA Cup as a substitute for Bruno N'Gotty in a 3-0 win at Vicarage Road. Name him.

548. This ex-Blacktown City Demons midfielder and Bolton Wanderers player from the 2007-08 season represented his country at Under-17 level and was a member of his nation's squad for the 2005 FIFA Under-17 World Championships. Who is he?

549. This player was invited to Bolton Wanderers' 2007-08 pre-season training camp in Austria and after impressing was signed on loan by Sammy Lee for one year with the option of a permanent deal at the end of the season. Name him.

550. From which French side did Bolton Wanderers purchase Abdoulaye Méité?

MIXED BAG – 7

551. Can you name the future Bolton striker who in March 1995 tested positive for cannabis thereby becoming the first ever Premier League footballer to fail a drug test?

552. In what position did the Trotters finish in the Premier League in season 2006-07 – 7th, 8th or 9th?

553. What award did Lofty the Lion win in season 1996-97?

554. Can you name the on-loan Liverpool midfielder who scored for Bolton Wanderers in a 2-1 League Cup 3rd Round win at Fulham on 26 September 2007?

555. What have Terry Allcock, Nat Lofthouse, Mixu Paatelainen and Neil Whatmore all got in common for Bolton Wanderers?

556. This Charlton Athletic "Mark" was the last ever opposition player to score a goal at Burnden Park. Name him.

557. On 31 October 2000 the Trotters beat Queens Park Rangers 3-1 in the Championship. Can you name the Bolton Wanderers goalkeeper who was sent off in the win at the Reebok?

558. Julian Darby and his brother played together in the Bolton Wanderers reserves in the early 1980s. Julian made over 250 appearances for the club but his brother was released without making an appearance for the first team. Name him.

559. In what year were Roy Evans, Nigel Spackman and Steve McMahon all linked with the vacant manager's job at Bolton Wanderers?

560. Can you recall the name of the former Bolton Wanderers striker who commuted from his home to Bolton via helicopter?

561.   Nat scored two goals on his debut for England but can you
        name their Eastern European opponents?

562.   In what year during the early 1960s was Nat appointed an
        assistant coach at Bolton?

563.   What "local" honour was bestowed on Nat on 2 December
        1989?

564.   In what year did Nat retire from international football?

565.   What is Nat's official title at Bolton Wanderers FC?

566.   In 1958 Nat broke Steve Bloomer's England goal scoring
        record. How many goals did Nat score for England – 28, 29 or
        30?

567.   What stand at the Reebok Stadium was named in honour of
        Nat – East, North or South?

568.   Was Nat awarded a CBE, MBE or an OBE in the 1994 New
        Year's Honours List?

569.   To the nearest 50, how many league goals did Nat score for
        the Trotters?

570.   Nat scored for England against these South American
        opponents during the 1954 FIFA World Cup Finals. Name
        them.

YOURI DJORKAEFF

571.   In what year did Youri Djorkaeff join Bolton Wanderers?

572.   Name the German Bundesliga club the Trotters signed Youri
        Djorkaeff from.

573.   Can you name the French club beginning with the letter "G"
        where Youri Djorkaeff began his professional career in 1984?

574.   Youri Djorkaeff made his Wanderers Premier League debut
        against a south coast club. Name them.

575.   Apart from the team in Q573, name any other one of the
        three French sides Youri played for during his career.

576.   Name the Italian Serie A side that Youri played for from
        1996-99.

577.   Youri scored his first and second goals for Bolton Wanderers
        in a 2-1 Premier League away win over this London club on
        23 March 2002. Can you recall the name of the team?

578.   In what year did Youri leave the Reebok Stadium?

579.   What Premier League club did Youri sign for after he left
        Bolton Wanderers?

580.   Can you name the three trophies Youri won playing for the
        French national team between 1993 and 2002?

THE BOSS – 4

581. When Ian Greaves took charge of Bolton Wanderers in 1974 the squad included a future Trotters manager. Name the player who later went on to manage the club.

582. Can you name the former Bolton Wanderers manager from the 1960s who was nicknamed "Nobbler" during his playing days?

583. When Bruce Rioch stepped down as Bolton Wanderers manager can you name the Premier League club he took charge of?

584. In June 2007 this former Bolton Wanderers manager from the 1990s was appointed the manager of the Danish Superliga side Randers FC. Name him.

585. Can you name the future Bolton Wanderers manager of the early 1970s that the legendary Joe Smith (1908-27, 492 league appearances and 277 league goals for the Trotters) spotted in a practice match at Bloomfield Road when he was the Blackpool manager and who was so impressed offered the player a trial before signing him for Blackpool?

586. This future Trotters manager captained his team to First Division Championship success, two League Cup Final wins and two European Cup triumphs. Who is he?

587. For how many games was Sammy Lee in charge of Bolton Wanderers before he left the club by mutual consent?

588. A former Bolton Wanderers manager has a stand named after him at Turf Moor. Name the Trotters ex-manager.

589. When Tom Mather (Wanderers manager 1915-19) left his position as Stoke City manager in June 1935 what north east club did he take charge of?

590. Name the Bolton Wanderers manager who guided the team to Division One play-off Final success in season 1994-95.

BURNDEN PARK – 2

591. What did Burnden Park play host to in 1901?

592. Can you recall the "City" who Bolton played at Burnden Park in an FA Cup 6th Round 2nd leg tie when the Burnden Park Disaster occurred?

593. How many fans sadly lost their lives in the Burnden Park Disaster – 33, 43 or 53?

594. Can you recall the name of the Government Ministry that requisitioned Burnden Park during World War II and used the Burnden Stand as storage space during the war?

595. To the nearest 5,000 what was the record crowd at Burnden Park?

596. Can you name the "City" that beat Bolton 4-2 in an FA Cup 5th Round tie at Burnden Park on 18 February 1933 when the record attendance for the ground was set?

597. Name the team that beat Bolton 3-2 in Round 4 of the FA Cup at Burnden Park on 4 February 1997 in the last ever FA Cup tie to be played at the ground. This team made it all the way to the semi-finals where they lost to Middlesbrough.

598. Can you name the London team that beat Bolton 2-0 in the quarter-final of the League Cup at Burnden Park on 8 January 1997 in the last ever League Cup tie to be played at the ground.

599. This colourful sounding player scored the last ever Cup goal for Bolton at Burnden Park. Name him.

600. This team walloped Bolton 6-0 at Burnden Park in the Premier League on 25 February 1996 in what was their last ever visit to the ground. Name them.

PLAYERS – 5

601. Name three players who have scored 100 or more League goals for Bolton Wanderers?

602. Can you name the former Bolton legend who in addition to his own nationality also holds Turkish citizenship, his Turkish name being Muhammed Yavuz?

603. At the start of the 2007-08 season Bolton Wanderers pur chased Daniel Braaten from Rosenborg. To the nearest £100,000 how much did he cost the Trotters?

604. Can you name the Tottenham Hotspur player who later went on to play for Wanderers who became the first opposing player to score a goal at the Reebok Stadium?

605. What is the record transfer fee paid out by Bolton Wanderers for a player?

606. Following on from Q605 can you name the player who holds the record for being Bolton's most expensive player?

607. Can you name the defender Bolton Wanderers obtained on loan from Liverpool and who appeared just once for the Trotters, a 3-1 defeat at home to Manchester City on 21 February 2004?

608. Wanderers purchased this player in the summer of 2004 only to sell him on to his former club Sunderland just three months later without him having played any senior games for the Trotters. Who is he?

609. Name either one of the two "Turner" brothers who in 1888 became the first set of brothers to play for the club.

610. How many international goals did Gary Speed score for Wales – 7, 8 or 9?

FINAL APPEARANCES - 2

*All you have to do here is match the Final with the year
the Trotters played in it*

611.	FA Cup Final	1886
612.	Sherpa Van Trophy Final	1929
613.	FA Cup Final	1986
614.	Lancashire Cup Final	2007
615.	Freight Rover Trophy Final	1958
616.	FA Cup Final	1912
617.	Lancashire Cup Final	1926
618.	Peace Cup Final	1953
619.	FA Cup Final	1948
620.	Lancashire Cup Final	1989

PLAYERS – 6

621. To what club did Bolton Wanderers sell Dietmar Hamann for a profit of £400,000 in the summer of 2006?

622. Can you name the Trotter who was controversially sent off in the last minute in their 2-1 Premier League loss at Arsenal on 21 September 2002 only for the Football Association panel to overturn the decision a few days later?

623. Can you name the former Trotters player and manager who grew up on Dudley's Wren's Nest estate and who went to school at Sycamore Green Primary School and Wren's Nest Secondary School?

624. This "Aidan" became the first substitute goalkeeper to be used by Bolton Wanderers when he replaced Keith Branagan who had suffered a knee injury in the 2-0 home defeat to Derby County on 30 October 1993. Name him.

625. What do Sasa Curcic, Nathan Blake, Neil Cox, Robbie Elliott, Mark Fish, Dean Holdsworth, Claus Jensen, Ricardo Gardner, Nicolas Anelka, Gavin McCann and Heidar Helguson all have in common for Bolton Wanderers?

626. In what Yorkshire city was Kevin Davies born?

627. Nicky Southall played for Bolton in the Premier League in season 2001-02. Can you name the character from the hit BBC TV comedy series, Only Fools and Horses, he is nicknamed after?

628. Name the Trotter who scored in the 2-1 home win over Reading at Burnden Park on 29 October 1996 and who had to go in goal for the Trotters during the game?

629. This future Bolton striker joined Tottenham Hotspur on 30 June 1995 from Crystal Palace for £4.5m, Spurs record transfer at the time. Who is he?

630. Name the Bolton midfielder about whom the Danish weekly gossip magazine "Se & Hor" ran a story during the 2002 FIFA World Cup Finals, stating that when the player was 13-years old he had returned home from school to find the bodies of his parents. His mother had been murdered by his father who then shot himself.

THE HISTORY – 7

631.   What was so remarkable about the 11 penalties Bolton was awarded in season 1899-90?

632.   What unwanted distinction does goalkeeper James Sutcliffe hold for Bolton Wanderers?

633.   In 1903-04 Bolton Wanderers found themselves back in Division Two along with two other founder members of the Football League. Name either one of the two Lancashire clubs.

634.   Can you name the Lancashire club Bolton finished runners-up to in Division Two in season 1904-05 thereby securing a return to top flight football?

635.   What was removed from the perimeter of the pitch at Burnden Park prior to the start of the 1905-06 season?

636.   In season 1908-09 despite being in the Second Division, Bolton's wage bill was the highest of all the Lancashire clubs. To the nearest £500 what was the total wage bill?

637.   At the end of the 1908-09 season Bolton Wanderers embarked on their first ever overseas tour. What European country did they visit winning all five of their games?

638.   In season 1910-11 Bolton won promotion back into Division One. Can you name the Midlands club they finished runners-up to in Division Two that season?

639.   What stand at Burnden Park had major renovation work carried out to it in season 1912-13?

640.   At the start of the 1913-14 season Bolton Wanderers splashed out a record transfer fee to bring Barnsley's centre forward George Lillycrop to Burnden Park. To the nearest £250 how much did Bolton pay for George's services?

641. Bolton beat this "City" 2-1 in the 4th Round of the League Cup at the Reebok on 30 November 2005. Can you name them?

642. Can you name the club with the "stingy" sounding nickname the Trotters beat 3-0 away in the FA Cup 3rd Round?

643. This Lancashire club hammered Bolton 4-1 on New Year's Eve 2006. Name them.

644. On 20 January 2006 the Trotters recorded their first Premier League win of the New Year. What "City" did they beat 2-0 at the Reebok?

645. Bolton beat Arsenal 1-0 at the Reebok in the 4th Round of the FA Cup on 28 January 2006. Who scored for the Trotters?

646. Name the Lancashire side that knocked Bolton out of the League Cup at the quarter-finals stage.

647. To the nearest five how many games did the Trotters play in total in all competitions in season 2005-06?

648. On 1 April 2006 Bolton lost 2-1 to Manchester United at the Reebok in the Premier League. Can you recall the striker who scored for the Trotters?

649. Bolton visted Middlesbrough for a Premier League game on 26 March 2006 in a fixture that produced seven goals. What was the score of the game?

650. This overseas central defender scored Bolton's first goal of 2006 in a 2-2 draw with Liverpool at the Reebok on 2 January. Can you name him?

BOLTON IN THE 1970s

651.   What is historically significant about the Bolton Wanderers
        team that beat Sheffield United 2-1 at Burnden Park in
        Division Two on 16 January 1971?

652.   Can you name the man who was appointed manager of Bolton
        Wanderers during the 1970-71 season but resigned just 18
        days later?

653.   What happened to Bolton Wanderers for the first time in the
        club's history at the end of the 1970-71 season?

654.   Can you recall what was erected at Burnden Park during the
        summer of 1977?

655.   Name the Bolton captain who was presented with the
        Division Three Championship trophy on 28 April 1973 after
        the Trotters defeated the already relegated Brentford 2-0 at
        Burnden Park in the last League game of the season.

656.   Whose goal for Bolton Wanderers in the 3-2 defeat to Ipswich
        Town at Burnden Park on 21 April 1979 in Division One won
        him the goal of the season award?

657.   What "first" resulted from Bolton's 3-2 FA Cup 3rd Round
        win over Stoke City at Burnden Park on 6 January 1974?

658.   On 5 October 1976 Bolton drew 2-2 with Fulham in a
        controversial League Cup 3rd Round replay at Burnden Park.
        Can you name the former England captain who was sent off?

659.   During the 1978-79 season Bolton splashed out a club record
        £250,000 to sign this player from Tottenham Hotspur. Who is
        he?

660.   During the 1970-71 season this former manager of
        Manchester United turned down the offer to manage Bolton
        Wanderers. Name him.

WINNERS – 2

*All you have to do here is match the trophy with the
year Bolton Wanderers won it*

661.	Football League Second Division	1955
662.	Football League First Division	2007
663.	Lancashire Cup	1926
664.	Sherpa Van Trophy	1973
665.	FA Cup	1978
666.	Football League Third Division	1997
667.	Central League (Reserves)	1925
668.	FA Premier League Asia Trophy	1948
669.	Reserve League North (Reserves)	1989
670.	Lancashire Cup	2005

671.   In what year did Jay-Jay leave Bolton Wanderers?

672.   What BBC Award did Jay-Jay win in both 2003 and 2004?

673.   Name the Turkish side Jay-Jay played for from 1996-98.

674.   How many FIFA World Cup Final tournaments did Jay-Jay
        appear in for Nigeria?

675.   Can you recall the slogan that paid tribute to Jay-Jay worn by
        many Bolton fans?

676.   What winners' medal did Jay-Jay win with the Super Eagles,
        Nigeria, during the summer of 1996?

677.   Who did Jay-Jay claim told him to sign for Hull City?

678.   Can you name the German league side Jay-Jay played for from
        1992-96?

679.   How many goals did Jay-Jay score for the Trotters – 16, 17 or
        18?

680.   In 2004 Jay-Jay released a DVD in which he teaches children at
        a football school the most difficult tricks in football. Name the
        DVD.

SEASON 2006-07 – 2

681.   Can you recall the "Rovers" Bolton beat 4-0 away in the 3rd Round of the FA Cup?

682.   Who scored twice for the Trotters in a 4-0 home Premier League win over West Ham United on 9 December 2006?

683.   He scored for Bolton in a 1-1 FA Cup 4th Round draw against Arsenal away. Name him.

684.   This London club knocked the Trotters out of the League Cup in the 3rd Round. Name them.

685.   Who was the only Trotter to score for the club in both the League Cup and FA Cup during the season?

686.   This "United" was the last team to defeat Bolton during the season. Name them.

687.   Of the 43 games the Trotters actually played during the season, how many did they win – 18, 19 or 20?

688.   During the season Bolton scored six penalty kicks. Gary Speed scored the last five of them but who scored their first?

689.   Bolton travelled to this North East club on 20 January 2007 for a Premier League game and were hammered 5-1. Can you name them?

690.   Bolton drew 2-2 with this Midlands club on the final day of the season at the Reebok. Name them.

THE BOSS – 5

691. To what legendary footballer did Tom Mather (Wanderers manager 1915-19) give his Stoke City debut in 1932?

692. This future Bolton Wanderers manager won the PFA Players' Player of the Year in 1975. Who is he?

693. Can you name the ex-Trotters boss who during his career played for a number of clubs including Aston Villa, Derby County, Everton and Seattle Sounders?

694. He was a player-manager at Bolton Wanderers, assistant manager at Plymouth Argyle and Hull City and joint-manager at Rotherham United during his career. Name him.

695. This former Bolton manager became a part-time coach under Sven Goran-Eriksson with England in 2001 before eventually leaving his club duties to go full-time with the national team in July 2004. Who is he?

696. When Ian Greaves was sacked as Bolton Wanderers manager in 1980 can you recall the "United" he took charge of?

697. This ex-Trotters boss is a consultant with the Football Association and was responsible for the appointment of Terry Venables as England coach in 1994 and was also a key figure in the appointment of Glenn Hoddle as England coach in 1996. Who is he?

698. Name the "Town" Walter Rowley (Wanderers manager 1944-50) took charge of from 1955-57.

699. This future England international and Bolton Wanderers manager was signed by Brian Clough and Peter Taylor for Derby County in August 1967. Who is he?

700. In which month during 2007 did Gary Megson take over as Bolton manager?

THE HISTORY – 8

701. Can you name Bolton's first £1 million player for whom the club paid £1.5m in August 1995?

702. How many different managers has Bolton Wanderers had since the end of the Second World War to include the appointment of Gary Megson – 18, 19 or 20?

703. In what season did the Trotters introduce Lofty the Lion?

704. Who became the first set of post-war brothers to play for the Bolton Wanderers first team?

705. In what position did the Trotters finish in the Premier League in season 2007-08?

706. Can you name any one of the three players who scored five goals for Bolton Wanderers in a game?

707. During the 1955-56 season goalkeeper Joe Dean had to leave the field of play in a game versus Wolverhampton Wanderers to have stitches inserted in a wound. Can you recall the Bolton striker who took his place in goal with the Trotters losing 4-2?

708. What is Bolton's biggest loss to Manchester United – 6-2, 7-2 or 8-2?

709. In 1994 this Finn became the first foreigner to be signed by Bolton Wanderers in 13 years. Who is he?

710. What claim to fame does James Martin have in the history of Bolton Wanderers and in particular Burnden Park's history?

MIXED BAG – 8

711.　Only four players have scored more goals for England than Nat Lofthouse. Name any three of the four.

712.　This "Tom" managed Bolton from 1915-19. Can you name him?

713.　In what position did the Trotters finish in the Premier League in season 2003-04 – 8th, 9th or 10th?

714.　On 18 January 1890 Bolton hammered this "Distillery" 10-2 in an FA Cup 1st Round tie. What UK city did they come from?

715.　This Bolton player captained his team at the 2006 African Cup of Nations. Name him.

716.　Who was Gary Speed once the assistant manager to at the Reebok Stadium?

717.　What is the name of the Bolton Wanderers official club mas cot?

718.　This future Bolton manager captained England once, in their 1-1 draw away to Iceland on 2 June 1982. Can you name him?

719.　In 2005 Bolton Wanderers won the Premier League Asia Trophy. What Asian country hosted the tournament?

720.　This former Trotter began his career at Drumchapel Amateurs before moving on to West Bromwich Albion, Manchester City, Nottingham Forest, Everton and numerous other clubs. Who is he?

BIG SAM ALLARDYCE - 3

721. Name the club Big Sam left to take up his appointment as the Bolton Wanderers manager.

722. Can you name the football magazine Big Sam writes a regular column for?

723. Big Sam appeared in only one game for West Bromwich Albion, coming on as a substitute against a north east club in November 1989. Name them.

724. Name the Lancashire club Big Sam captained to promotion from Division Four in season 1986-87.

725. What was the highest end of season league placing Big Sam guided Blackpool to?

726. Can you name the Division Three club Big Sam guided to pro motion after finishing top of Division Three at the end of the 1997-98 season in which the club broke several club and national records, winning the title by 19 points and becoming the first post-war side to win promotion in mid-March?

727. In what year did Big Sam leave the Reebok Stadium as the manager of Bolton Wanderers?

728. What club did Big Sam become the manager of when he left his position as manager of the Trotters?

729. To the nearest five how many league goals did Big Sam score for Bolton Wanderers?

730. Name the two clubs Big Sam both played for and managed.

PLAYERS - 7

731.   This former Trotter was nicknamed Toffe during his playing days. Who is he?

732.   At the start of the 2007-08 season Bolton Wanderers released Tal Ben-Haim on a Free Transfer. What club did he sign for?

733.   Can you name the Jamaican-born player the Trotters signed for the 2001-02 season?

734.   Can you name the future Bolton Wanderers striker who scored a hat-trick in his side's shock 3-2 FA Cup 4th Round win over the Trotters at Burnden Park on 23 February 1997?

735.   This "Michael" (Wanderers 2001-03) is ranked fourth in the club record books for the record number of goals scored against appearances (minimum of 50 appearances) with a goal every 135 minutes (46 goals in 68 appearances with 44 sub appearances). Name him.

736.   Can you name the "Chris" who was allocated the No.45 shirt for the Trotters during the 2007-08 season?

737.   When Jussi Jaaskelainen was sent off in a Premier League clash with Newcastle United on 13 October 2001 at the Reebok the Trotters had not named a goalkeeper among their substitutes. Which Danish midfielder took over in goal?

738.   When this player signed for Bolton Wanderers in August 2006 it caused such a stir in his homeland that a television channel was set up to enable his fans to check on his progress in the Premier League. Who is he?

739.   This Bolton Wanderers goalkeeper won the Best Goalkeeper award in the Gulf Cup on three occasions. Who is he?

740.   In season 2003-04 this Trotter scored against two of his former clubs in a Premier League game. Who is he?

THE BOSS – 6

741. Can you name the future Bolton Wanderers manager who took charge of Bradford City after their manager George Mulhall left to take charge of Bolton Wanderers in May 1981?

742. This former Bolton Wanderers manager guided Leeds United to the European Cup Final in season 1974-75. Who is he?

743. This former Bolton Wanderers manager scored 24 goals in season 1967-68 to help Luton Town to the Fourth Division title. Who is he?

744. What "City" did Tom Mather (Wanderers manager 1915-19) win the Third Division North title with in 1926-27 and the Second Division title in 1931-32?

745. Colin Todd (Wanderers manager 1996-99) managed this Yorkshire club from 2004-07. Name them.

746. This Wanderers manager from the 1980s played for Workington, Grimsby Town, Charlton Athletic and Bolton Wanderers during his career. Who is he?

747. This Bolton manager from the 1970s won a First Division winners' medal with Burnley in season 1959-60 and is regarded as one of the greatest ever players to have played for Burnley. Name him.

748. What "Town" did Ian Greaves manage from 1968-74 before he was appointed the manager of Bolton Wanderers in 1974?

749. Who is the longest serving manager in the history of Bolton Wanderers?

750. Walter Rowley stepped down as Bolton Wanderers Manager in 1950 having served the club for 37 years as a player, coach and manager. Two years later his health returned and he took charge of a north east club. Can you name them?

751. Can you name the Bolton goalkeeper who was in goal for the Trotters for Bolton's first ever European away game against the Bulgarian side Lokomotiv Plovdiv in season 2006-07?

752. This future Trotter was signed by Watford manager Graham Taylor for a club record transfer fee of £1.5m mid-way through the 1999-2000. Who is he?

753. Can you name the Bolton defender who won his first England Under-21 cap against the Netherlands in February 2004?

754. Prior to signing for Bolton Wanderers in the summer of 2007 this player had played for several clubs including RSC Anderlecht (Belgium, 2003-06) and AS Roma (Italy, on loan in 2007). Can you name him?

755. This future Trotter was a member of the Sunderland side which won the Division One Championship title and promotion to the Premier League with 105 points in season 1998-99. Name him.

756. In the summer of 2005 this Bolton Wanderers striker took part in the annual Toulon tournament scoring a hat-trick for his country's Under-20 team in their match against South Korea. Who is he?

757. This Bolton Wanderers player was signed by the club in the summer of 2007 and was born in Tetovo, Macedonia, SFR Yugoslavia in 1986. Name him.

758. Can you name the Irish midfielder Bolton Wanderers loaned out to Sheffield Wednesday for most of the 2004-05 season (he won his first cap for the Republic of Ireland on 1 March 2006 while at Bolton)?

759. Can you name the Bolton Wanderers player from season 2007-08 who made his international debut for his country as a second half substitute against the United Arab Emirates and scored in 2007?

760. During his school days this member of the 2007-08 Bolton strike force was the third fastest schoolboy sprinter for the UK and was earmarked as a potential Olympic athlete. Can you name him?

761. On Boxing Day 1914 Bolton recorded their biggest away league win to date, a 7-1 victory. Can you name the Midlands club who were on the receiving end?

762. During the 1919-20 season Bolton had to cancel a number of their less important away games due to a strike by a certain group of workers. Can you name the striking workforce?

763. What new rule, connected with throw-ins, was introduced prior to the start of the 1920-21 season?

764. At the start of the 1920-21 season Bolton Wanderers splashed out a record transfer fee to bring Luton Town full back John Elvey to Burnden Park. To the nearest £500 how much did Bolton pay for John's services?

765. On 30 April 1921 this "Joe" scored his 38th league goal of the season to set the club record of most goals by a player in a season. Name him.

766. This team beat Bolton 2-1 in the 1921 Lancashire Cup Final played at Old Trafford. Name them.

767. What Cup did Bolton win for a fourth time in season 1921-22?

768. This "David" became the first five-figure player when Bolton sold him to Arsenal in season 1928-29 for £10,750. Can you name him?

769. In March 1930 Bolton signed a young player from Brierly Hill Alliance who went on to become a household name in Bolton. Name this "Ray".

770. In June 1932 this "Harold" left Bolton Wanderers for Middlesbrough in a £4,000 transfer deal after scoring 122 goals in 165 League and Cup games for the Trotters. Can you name him?

EL HADJI-DIOUF

771.   In what year did El Hadji-Diouf sign for Bolton Wanderers?

772.   How old was El Hadji-Diouf when he made his debut for the
       Trotters?

773.   El Hadji-Diouf made his Wanderers debut against this "United"
       in the Premier League. Name them.

774.   From what Premier League club did the Trotters sign
       El Hadji-Diouf?

775.   Name the "United" El Hadji-Diouf scored his first goal for the
       Trotters against.

776.   Can you name the French club the team in Q774 signed El
       Hadji-Diouf from?

777.   How many Premier League goals did El Hadji-Diouf score in
       his first season with the Trotters – 8, 9 or 10?

778.   In what year did El Hadji-Diouf first play for Senegal in a
       senior international?

779.   What did El Hadji-Diouf do on 15 September 2005 that no
       other Trotter had done in the history of the club?

780.   Which Premier League club did El Hadji-Diouf join in the
       summer of 2008?

NICOLAS ANELKA

781. Prior to signing for Bolton Wanderers, which club did Nicolas Anelka play for?

782. In which year did Nicolas join the Trotters?

783. At which French club did Nicolas begin his professional football career?

784. From 2001-02, which English club was Nicolas on loan to?

785. Nicolas played for this Premier League club from 1997-99. Can you name them?

786. Can you name the team Nicolas signed for after he left the club in Q785?

787. Apart from being a club record transfer how did Nicolas create football history when he signed for Chelsea for £15 million on 11 January 2008?

788. What individual Award did Nicolas win in season 1998-99?

789. Against which one of his former clubs did Nicolas score his first goal for Bolton Wanderers in a Premier League game played at the Reebok on 25 November 2006?

790. Name the former England boss who once signed Nicolas Anelka.

TAL BEN HAIM

791. Which county was Tal Ben Haim born in?

792. Prior to signing for the Trotters, which club did Tal Ben Haim play for?

793. In which year did he move to the Reebok Stadium?

794. How many League appearances did Tal Ben Haim make for Bolton?

795. In what year did Tal Ben Haim leave Bolton Wanderers?

796. How many Premier League goals did Tal Ben Haim score for Bolton?

797. Can you recall the trophy Tal Ben Haim won in the 2002-03 season with the team in Q792?

798. In which year was Tal Ben Haim first capped by his country at full international level?

799. Can you recall Bolton's 2005-06 UEFA Cup opponents when Tal Ben Haim was handed the captain's armband?

800. How much did Bolton pay for Tal Ben Haim - £150,000, £200,000 or £250,000?

THE BOSS – 7

801. Can you name the ex-Trotters boss who became the first Scottish (by virtue of his father's birthplace) captain to be born in England?

802. Name the former Bolton Wanderers manager who won promotion with Hartlepool United, Derby County and Nottingham Forest plus two Scottish Under-23 caps.

803. He played 110 games for Aberdeen, scoring 30 goals, and helped the team to runners-up position in Scottish League Division One in season 1955-56 and Scottish League Cup winners the same season. In 1981 he was appointed the manager of Bolton Wanderers. Who is he?

804. This former Bolton Wanderers manager guided Mansfield Town to promotion in 1985-86 and won the Freight Rover Trophy with the same club at Wembley in 1986-87. Who is he?

805. This future Bolton Wanderers manager played his final game for his club on 1 May 1971 against Manchester United in what would be the last game played by this seaside club in the top flight of English football. Name him.

806. Stan Anderson, Bolton Wanderers manager (1980-81), managed Middlesbrough from 1966-73. Can you name the England World Cup winner who succeeded him as boss of Boro in April 1973?

807. In June 2005 Sammy Lee was appointed as the assistant manager to Sam Allardyce at Bolton Wanderers following the departure of Big Sam's former assistant who moved to Derby County. Whose position did Sammy fill?

808. What seaside club did Tom Mathers move to after he left his position as Bolton Wanderers manager in 1919?

809. Can you name the future Bolton Wanderers manager who won a World Cup winners' medal as part of the England squad at the 1966 World Cup Finals?

810. Former Bolton Wanderers boss Colin Todd played for Derby County, Sunderland, Everton, Birmingham City, Nottingham Forest, Oxford United, Vancouver Whitecaps and Luton Town. Which one of these eight clubs did he once manage?

FREDI BOBIC

811. Prior to signing for Bolton Wanderers, which German club did Fredi Bobic play for?

812. Can you recall the year in which Fredi was on loan to Bolton?

813. How many Premier League appearances did he make for the Trotters – 15, 16 or 17?

814. At which German club did Fredi Bobic begin his professional career?

815. After ending his loan spell at the Reebok Stadium, which German club did he sign for?

816. How many Premier League goals did Fredi score for Bolton?

817. To the nearest five, how many full international caps did Fredi win for Germany?

818. Although Fredi played international football for Germany he was not born in Germany. In which country was he born?

819. Can you name the season Fredi finished the top goal scorer in the German Bundesliga with 17 goals or the team he played for at the time?

820. Name the Croatian club he signed for in 2006.

PLAYERS – 8

821. To the nearest £250,000 how much did Bolton Wanderers pay for Gary Speed?

822. Can you name the 2004 African Cup of Nations winner who joined Bolton Wanderers later the same year?

823. This "Bill", an Irish international striker, arrived in the summer of 1960 from Manchester City. Name him.

824. Name the Trotter who in season 1978-79 topped the First Division's goal scoring charts with 24 goals.

825. Can you name the player to whom Sam Allardyce offered the opportunity to train with Bolton Wanderers in their Italian training camp ahead of the 2003-04 Premier League season and who then impressed enough during the pre-season visit to Malta to be offered a one year contract with the Trotters?

826. He made his debut with Bolton Wanderers in their 2-1 Carling Cup away win over Fulham on 26 September 2007 and was in goal for the Trotters when they drew 2-2 with FC Bayern Munich in the Allianz Arena on 8 November 2007. Who is he?

827. Can you name the former Trotter who retired from international football in 2002 having made 82 appearances for his national side and scoring 28 goals in nine years?

828. During the summer of 2007 this Bolton striker scored a cheeky penalty for his country's Under-21 side against England's Under-21s by chipping the ball over the head of Manchester City goalkeeper Joe Hart. Who is he?

829. This Bolton Wanderers striker from the 2007-08 season holds a National School Boy record having scored nine goals for Northumberland in a county match against South Yorkshire. Who is he?

830. During the 2006-07 season this young Bolton Wanderers goalkeeper was loaned to Accrington Stanley for whom he played eight games. Name him.

BOLTON IN THE 1980s

831. In what season during the 1980s did the Football League re-introduce play-off promotion games for the first time since the 1890s with the Trotters losing their Division Three play-off game over two legs to Aldershot?

832. In season 1981-82 former Bolton goalkeeper Jim McDonagh returned to Burnden Park in a deal that gave the Trotters £90,000 and saw this Trotters goalkeeper named "Mike" move to Everton. Name him.

833. Prior to the 1981-82 season this striker joined his former Bolton team-mate Frank Worthington at First Division Birmingham City in a deal worth £340,000 which made him the club's record sale at the time. Who is he?

834. Can you name the player, a European Cup winner, who joined Bolton Wanderers prior to the start of the 1980-81 season for £150,000 from Everton?

835. Can you recall the season in which Burnden Park celebrated its 90th birthday or the "United" the Trotters drew 1-1 with in the opening game of that season at Burnden Park?

836. On the opening day of the 1985-86 season this "Tony" scored the Trotters 250th goal in the Third Division. Who is he?

837. On 22 August 1987 the Trotters recorded their first win in a Division Four game. Can you name the Welsh side they beat 1-0 at Burnden Park?

838. This "George" managed Bolton in season 1981-82. Can you name him?

839. Can you name the Bolton striker who had to take over in goal in the Trotters' 1-1 Division Three away draw with Rotherham United on 11 February 1984?

840. This "Tony" scored five times for Bolton against Walsall in an 8-1 Division Three home win on 10 September 1983. Name him.

PER FRANDSEN

841. Per had two spells at the Reebok stadium, but in which year did the first spell begin?

842. In what year did he leave the Trotters for the first time?

843. Following on from Q842, can you name the team he joined?

844. To the nearest 50, how many League appearances did Frandsen make for the Trotters during his two spells with the club?

845. Name the season he signed for Bolton for a second time.

846. In which position did Per Frandsen play for Bolton Wanderers?

847. To the nearest five, how many League goals did he score for the Trotters?

848. At which Lancashire club did Per end his professional football career?

849. Can you name the Danish club where Per began his professional football career?

850. Between 1990 and 2003, how many international caps did he win for Denmark, to the nearest 10?

RICARDO GARDNER

851.   Can you name the team from the Jamaican National Premier
        League that the Trotters signed Ricardo from?

852.   In what position does Ricardo Gardner play for the Trotters?

853.   Name the year in which Bolton Wanderers signed Ricardo.

854.   In his first season at Bolton, how many League appearances did
        Gardner make – 20, 30 or 40?

855.   How old was Ricardo when he made his debut for the team
        in Q851?

856.   Against which Midlands club did Ricardo make his League
        debut for the Trotters?

857.   Ricardo was first capped by Jamaica in this year. Name it.

858.   What type of music is Ricardo very much involved in,
        promoting the work of the artist Erup?

859.   What honour was Ricardo handed in 2005?

860.   At what major football tournament did Ricardo come to
        prominence leading to his move to the Reebok shortly after
        it?

THE HISTORY – 10

861. Can you name the Wanderers midfielder who scored the first ever goal at the Reebok Stadium when he netted a penalty against Tottenham Hotspur in a 1-1 Premier League draw on 23 September 1997?

862. Who was the last pair of brothers to play for Bolton Wanderers when they played against Bury in a 1-0 Worthington Cup defeat on 2 October 2002?

863. Substitutes were first introduced to English Football in season 1965-66 and Wanderers have the distinction of being involved in the first game that involved a substitution. Can you name their London opponents on 21 August 1965?

864. Can you recall the name of the Electronics Company that adorned the Bolton kit in seasons 1983-86 as the club's official sponsor?

865. What claim to fame does striker David Jack have in the history of Bolton Wanderers after joining the club in December 1920 from Plymouth Argyle?

866. Can you name three players who all played for Bolton Wanderers during their career and who have all been included in the Queens Honours List?

867. Name the player, who when he made his debut for the club in March 2000, became the first Academy scholar to make the first team since the Trotters gained Academy status in 1998.

868. On 15 February 1977 Everton beat Bolton 1-0 in the League Cup semi-final 2nd leg to go through to the Final 2-1 aggregate after the 1st leg ended 1-1. What was significant about the attendance of 50,413 at Burnden Park for the game?

869. When Bolton Wanderers played in the 1994-95 League Cup Final can you name the drinks company that sponsored the competition that season?

870. Can you name Bolton's fierce rivals whose 1-0 loss at Burnden Park on the last day of the 1992-93 season sent them down into the Third Division (the old Division Four following the creation of the FA Premier League in season 1992-93)?

STELIOS GIANNAKOPOULOS

871.   What is Stelios's full name?

872.   In which year did Bolton sign the Greek midfielder?

873.   Prior to signing for the Trotters, which club did he play for?

874.   At which Greek club did he begin his professional career?

875.   Can you name the Greek side beginning with the letter "P" that he played for from 1993-96?

876.   In his first season as a Trotter, how many League appearances did Stelios make or how many League goals did he score?

877.   Against which "United" did Giannakopoulos make his League debut for Bolton Wanderers?

878.   In what year did he win his first international cap for Greece?

879.   What competition did Stelios win with Greece in the summer of 2004?

880.   What unusual Premier League record was Stelios a part of when he was replaced by Ibrahim Ba in a Premiership game for Bolton Wanderers on 31 January 2004?

JUSSI JAASKELAINEN

881.   What nationality is Jussi Jaaskelainen?

882.   In which year did Bolton sign Jussi Jaaskelainen?

883.   Prior to signing for the Trotters, what club did Jussi
       Jääskeläinen play for?

884.   How much did Bolton pay for Jussi - £100,000, £200,000 or
       £300,000?

885.   Can you name the two club awards he won for the 2006-07
       season?

886.   In what year during the late 1990s did he win his first
       international cap for his country?

887.   Name the club, former European Cup winners, Jussi made his
       300th appearance against for Bolton Wanderers on New Year's
       Day 2007.

888.   Can you name the Trotters manager who signed Jussi for the
       club?

889.   Against which London club did Jussi make his League debut
       for the Trotters?

890.   In what season was he voted the Barclaycard Premier League
       Goalkeeeper of the Year?

PLAYERS - 9

891.   This former Trotter's father, Jean, played for France at the 1966
         FIFA World Cup Finals in England and also coached the
         Armenian national team. Name the former Wanderer.

892.   At the start of the 2007-08 season Bolton Wanderers released
         Blazej Augustyn on a Free Transfer. What club did he sign for?

893.   Can you name either one of Nat Lofthouse's two team mates
         who played alongside him for England against Northern
         Ireland in November 1953 and October 1954?

894.   This "Andy" (Wanderers 1991-94) is ranked third in the club
         record books for the record number of goals scored against
         appearances (minimum of 20 goals) with a goal every
         128 minutes (55 goals in 78 appearances with nine sub
         appearances). Name him.

895.   After what tournament did Jay-Jay Okocha retire from
         international football?

896.   This Bolton Wanderers youth team goalkeeper made his
         debut for the Trotters in their 3-0 FA Cup 3rd Round win over
         Watford at Vicarage Road on 7 January 2006. He came on as
         a substitute but not for Ian Walker in the Trotters goal, instead
         he found himself having to play the final few minutes of the
         game as a striker. Who is he?

897.   Can you name the player Bolton Wanderers signed on loan in
         March 2000 and sent home to Australia after learning that had
         been involved in an armed robbery in Melbourne back in
         1995?

898.   Name any two of the three England internationals, who played
         for Bolton Wanderers at some point during their careers, who
         starred in the movie "Hero," the official 1986 FIFA World Cup
         movie.

899.   Can you name the Bolton Wanderers player signed for season
         2007-08 whose younger brother was already playing in the
         Premier League?

900.   Name the Trotter defender in 2007-08 who won an Intertoto
         Cup winners' medal in season 2000-01.

EIDUR GUDJOHNSEN

901. In which year did Bolton Wanderers sign Eidur Gudjohnsen?

902. To the nearest 20 how many League appearances did Eidur Gudjohnsen make in his time at the Trotters?

903. In which Scandinavian country was he born?

904.. Can you name the Dutch side Eidur played for from 1994-96?

905. Name the year in which Eidur left the Reebok Stadium.

906. After leaving the Trotters which club did Eidur Gudjohnsen sign for?

907. In 2006 Eidur Gudjohnsen left the team in Q906 and signed for this side. Name them.

908. How many goals did Eidur score for Bolton – 25, 26 or 27?

909. Can you recall the "City" Eidur made his League debut with the Trotters against?

910. To the nearest £1m, how much did Bolton receive for Eidur when he joined the team in Q906?

JOHN McGINLAY

911.   Can you name the year John signed for Bolton Wanderers?

912.   To the nearest 25 how many League appearances did John make for the Trotters?

913.   Prior to signing for Bolton which London club did John McGinlay play for?

914.   In which year did John leave the Trotters?

915.   How many League goals did John score during his time at Bolton – 77, 87 or 97?

916.   Name the Yorkshire "City " John signed for when he left Bolton Wanderers in a £625,000 transfer, a record buy for the team at the time.

917.   To the nearest five, how many senior international appearances did he make for Scotland?

918.. Can you name the North American club that John McGinlay played for in 2000?

919.   John played for this "Athletic" club in season 1998-99. Can you name them?

920.   During his football career John played for a number of different clubs. Can you name any two of the teams he played for not mentioned above?

PLAYERS – 10

921. Can you name the goalkeeper whose transfer from Lyn Oslo to Bolton Wanderers in January 2006 was one of the transfers targeted by the Stevens Inquiry report in June 2007?

922. This player scored his first two goals for Bolton Wanderers in their 3rd Round FA Cup 4-0 away win over Doncaster Rovers on 6 January 2007. Name him.

923. This tigerish Bolton midfielder had his contract at the Reebok ended in the summer of 2003 and, after being released early from prison in July 2003, joined Tianjin Taida in China. Who is he?

924. When this future Bolton Wanderers defender appeared on MTV's Footballers Cribs, he revealed he calls himself "Sweetboy" and called his girlfriend (Emma Pritchard) "Sweetgirl". Who is he?

925. Can you name the Bolton striker in season 2007-08 who made his debut for Lillestrom in 1998, strangely wearing the club's No.1 jersey?

926. This boyhood Bolton Wanderers supporter made his debut for the Trotters as a substitute for Colin Hendry in the First Division match against Sheffield United on the final day of the 2000-01 season. Name him.

927. Can you name the member of the Bolton Wanderers squad in season 2007-08 who is also an accomplished mandolin player and vocalist and worked with the American singer, Prince?

928. This future Bolton Wanderers player was one of three players from the Swedish national team sent home in September 2006 because they broke a curfew during a night out. Name him.

929. Can you name the "City" Bolton Wanderers loaned Ricardo Vaz Tê to in March 2007 for one month?

930. This future Trotter signed for Aston Villa from Sunderland in 2003. Who is he?

HENRIK PEDERSEN

931. In which year did Bolton Wanderers sign Pedersen?

932. Can you name the Danish side the Trotters purchased Henrik from?

933. In which year did Henrik leave the Reebok Stadium?

934. When he left the Reebok Stadium can you name the club he signed for?

935. To the nearest 30 how many League appearances did Henrik Pedersen make for the Trotters?

936. When he played for the team in Q932 Henrik was given the nickname "Tomrer". What type of occupation using craftsman's tools is a Tomrer?

937. Against which "City" did Henrik make his League debut for Bolton Wanderers?

938. How many League goals did Henrik score during his time with the Trotters?

939. During his time with Bolton Wanderers Henrik was loaned out to this Danish side. Name them.

940. What type of bird-related goal celebration was Henrik famous for?

FRANK WORTHINGTON - 2

941.   Can you name the only team Frank both played for and managed?

942.   Frank enjoyed the company of ladies during his playing career and with a somewhat tongue-in-cheek front cover for his autobiography Frank is depicted smiling as he contemplates putting lumps of sugar in a cup of tea. What was the title of his book?

943.   Frank was a First Division runner-up to Liverpool in season 1983-84 with this club. Name them.

944.   Can you name the Swedish club Frank played briefly for in 1980?

945.   In what year during the late 1980s did Frank retire from playing?

946.   Name the "County" where he ended his playing career.

947.   How many goals did Frank score for England – 2, 3 or 4?

948.   Frank played for this North East club during the 1982-83 season. Name them.

949.   Which one of his many clubs did Frank play the most League games for?

950.   To the nearest 50 how many career League goals did Frank score?

THE MANAGEMENT GAME

All you have to do here is match the player with Bolton Wanderers connections to the club he later managed in his career

951.	Sam Allardyce	Southampton
952.	Asa Hartford	Grestley Rovers
953.	Tommy Wright	Blackburn Rovers
954.	Peter Barnes	Exeter City
955.	Len Cantello	Plymouth Argyle
956.	Stuart Gray	Blackpool
957.	Brian Kidd	Runcorn
958.	Peter Shilton	Shrewsbury Town
959.	John McGinlay	Linfield
960.	Neil McNab	Oldham Town

BOLTON WANDERERS
v MANCHESTER UNITED

961. To the nearest 10 how many times has Bolton Wanderers played Manchester United at home including the 1-0 win over the Red Devils on 24 November 2007?

962. Following on from the question in Q961, to the nearest five how many of these games has the Trotters won?

963. What is Bolton's biggest win over United – 6-1, 6-2 or 6-3?

964. In what season did the two clubs meet in the First Division for the last time?

965. Prior to becoming Manchester United in 1902 the club was known as Newton Heath. How many times did the Trotters meet the Heathens – 6, 8 or 10?

966. In how many different Divisions have the Trotters met United (the Premier League is the same as the First Division)?

967. The two sides last met in the FA cup in season 1990-91. What was the score of the game?

968. In what season did the two clubs meet in a Premier League game for the first time?

969. Prior to the 2007-08 season in what season did the Trotters last beat United in a home game?

970. Following on from Q969, what was the score in the game?

MR CONSISTENCY - 3

All you have to do here is associate the player (and his appearances) with the season in which he played the most games for the Trotters

971.	John Hulme, 40	1992-93
972.	Bryan Edwards, 44	1998-99
973.	Michael Ricketts, 42	1960-61
974.	Keith Branagan, 60	1989-90
975.	Jim McDonagh, 47	1995-96
976.	Eddie Hopkinson, 50	1955-56
977.	Kevin Nolan, 42	1970-71
978.	Claus Jensen, 54	1982-83
979.	Phil Brown/Julian Darby, 62	2001-02
980.	Jimmy Phillips, 45	2004-05

PHIL NEAL

981. In which year did Phil sign for Bolton Wanderers as player/manager?

982. How many League appearances did Phil make for the Trotters – 64, 65 or 66?

983. Prior to joining Liverpool in 1974 which Town did Phil play for?

984. How many First Division Championship winners' medals did Phil win with Liverpool?

985. Phil once managed this Welsh team. Can you name them?

986. Which one of the European trophies was the only one Phil failed to win with the Reds?

987. Against which one of the British Home international countries did Phil make his full England debut against?

988. Can you recall the trophy Phil guided Bolton to victory in during season 1988-89?

989. To the nearest 10, how many full international caps did Phil win for England?

990. When Phil left Bolton he did so to take-up the position of assistant coach to the England manager. Can you name the England boss at the time?

PLAYERS IN – SEASON 2007-08

*All you have to do here is associate the player with the club
Bolton Wanderers obtained him from, either through a free
transfer/purchase/loan*

991.	Zoltan Harsanyi	Rosenborg
992.	Gerald Cid	FC Zurich
993.	Blerim Dzemaili	Portsmouth
994.	Danny Guthrie	Nantes
995.	Mikel Alonso	Vasas
996.	Heidar Helguson	Fulham
997.	Christian Wilhelmsson	Real Sociedad
998.	Adam Bogdan	FC Senec
999.	Daniel Braaten	Liverpool
1000.	Andy O'Brien	Bordeaux

ANSWERS

THE HISTORY - I

1.   1874

2.   Christ Church FC

3.   1877

4.   11

5.   Premier League clubs 2007-08 - Aston Villa, Blackburn Rovers, Derby County and Everton plus Accrington, Burnley, Notts County, Preston North End, Stoke, West Bromwich Albion, Wolverhampton Wanderers

6.   Four

7.   1923

8.   It was the first ever FA cup final played at Wembley Stadium

9.   1995-96

10. 2005-06

THE KIT

11. Red

12. 1980

13. Knight Security

14. White shirts with navy blue shorts

15. 1970s

16. It consists of the initials of the club in the shape of a ball, with red and blue ribbons beneath

17. The red rose of Lancashire

18. The crest of the city of Bolton

19. Normid superstore

20. The Bolton Evening News

MIXED BAG – I

21. Phil Gartside (Chairman) whose role was to announce a fictitious South American signing for Bolton Wanderers

22. Norwich City (1984-85)

23. Thailand national football team, Birmingham City and Manchester

City

24. 6th

25. 15

26. 159 (285 goals in 503 appearances)

27. Wrexham

28. Nat Lofthouse (Lofty the Lion)

29. Johann Smith

30. Crowd Segregation (Bolton won 2-1)

BOLTON WANDERERS v PRESTON NORTH END

31. 67

32. 71

33. 27

34. 22

35. 10 (Preston North End 9 Bolton Wanderers 1 – 1887-88)

36. Six (6-1)

37. 2000-01 (Division One play-off Final)

38. The FA Cup

39. Ewood Park (Blackburn Rovers)

40. Associate Members Cup

MR CONSISTENCY - I

41.	Warren Joyce, 55	1986-87
42.	Gundi Bergsson, 51	2000-01
43.	Julian Darby, 56	1991-92
44.	Gary Speed, 42	2006-07
45.	Jimmy Phillips, 58	1994-95
46.	Alan Gowling, 45	1980-81
47.	Per Frandsen, 43	1997-98
48.	Barry Siddall, 50	1973-74
49.	Ivan Campo/Kevin Nolan, 44	2003-04
50.	Doug Holden, 45	1959-60

LEGEND – NAT LOFTHOUSE - I

51. 1939
52. 1941 (on 22nd March in a 5-1 win over Bury, wartime League Football)
53. Two
54. Chelsea (he scored twice in a 4-3 loss)
55. 33
56. 1950 (on 22nd November)
57. The Lion of Vienna
58. He scored twice for England in their dramatic 3-2 win over Austria in Vienna on 25th May 1952
59. 1953
60. 452

BURNDEN PARK - I

61. 1895
62. The Railway End
63. 1946 (9 March)
64. To make way for a new Normid superstore
65. John McGinlay
66. The First Division Championship trophy
67. 1997
68. Charlton Athletic (a 4-1 win on 25 April 1997)
69. Auld Lang Syne
70. ASDA

WINNERS – I

71.	Lancashire Cup	1886
72.	FA Cup	1923
73.	Football League War Cup North	1945
74.	Football League War Cup	1945
75.	Lancashire Cup	1990
76.	FA Charity Shield	1958

77.	FA Cup	1929
78.	Lancashire Cup	1988
79.	Football League Second Division	1909
80.	FA Cup	1958

BOLTON IN THE 1990s

81.	1990-91
82.	Swansea City – Tony Philliskirk
83.	Andy Walker
84.	John McGinlay
85.	John McGinlay
86.	1994-95
87.	16 years
88.	Fabian De Freitas
89.	Wolverhampton Wanderers
90.	Reading

BOLTON IN THE 1960s

91.	It was the first televised League game to be shown live
92.	Birmingham City
93.	Dennis Stevens
94.	Wyn Davies
95.	Manchester United and Everton
96.	He (Mr Fussey) blew his whistle for full time but was corrected by a linesman
97.	They changed to an all-white kit
98.	Eddie Hopkinson
99.	Nat Lofthouse was officially appointed manager of Wanderers (he had spent the previous four months as caretaker manager)
100.	Roger Hunt

KEVIN NOLAN

| 101. | 1998 |

102. 17 (born on 24 June 1982, debut on 4 March 2000)

103. Charlton Athletic (as a substitute in a 2-0 home defeat in Division One)

104. 2000 (January)

105. Crewe Alexandra (on 9 December 2000 in a 4-0 home win in Division One)

106. Manchester United (at Old Trafford)

107. Eight

108. Season 2005-06

109. He scored for Bolton Wanderers in an away European game (in one of the three major European club competitions)

110. Jay-Jay Okocha

THREE LIONS ON A SHIRT

111. Nat Lofthouse (33 caps)

112. Michael Ricketts (2002)

113. Two

114. Thomas Banks

115. David Weir (2 caps)

116. 26

117. Eight

118. Ray Parry (2 caps)

119. Eddie Hopkinson

120. Jimmy Armfield

THE HISTORY – 2

121. Schoolmaster (at Christ Church School)

122. Fletcher Street Men (17 April 1888)

123. The Vicar

124. The Gladstone Hotel (William Gladstone)

125. 1881-82

126. Blackburn Rovers

127. Pikes Lane

128.   They booed him off the pitch (he was also assaulted at the Railway Station)

129.   Lancashire Cup, Bolton Charity Cup and Derbyshire Charity Cup

130.   Anfield (Liverpool was not formed until 1892 and Everton played their home games at Anfield up to 1892)

PLAYERS – I

131.   Ivan Campo (winner with Real Madrid)

132.   Robert Sissons

133.   They were all born in Bolton and played for the club

134.   Youri Djorkaeff (Wanderers 2002-04)

135.   Sam Allardyce

136.   Zero

137.   Abdoulaye Méïté

138.   Stig Tofting (Wanderers 2002-03)

139.   Eusebio

140.   Jlloyd Samuel (from Aston Villa)

THE HISTORY – 3

141.   11

142.   Eddie Hopkinson

143.   Floodlights

144.   The FA Charity Shield

145.   Tom Finney

146.   An ankle injury

147.   None

148.   1,507

149.   Barnsley

150.   Tottenham Hotspur

FINAL APPEARANCES - I

151.   FA Cup Final   1923

152.   League Cup Final   1995

153.	FA Premier League Asia Trophy Final	2005
154.	Lancashire Cup Final	1990
155.	FA Cup Final	1894
156.	League Cup Final	2004
157.	Lancashire Cup Final	1925
158.	FA Cup Final	1904
159.	Football League War Cup Final	1945
160.	Lancashire Cup Final	1988

THE FOREIGN LEGION - 1

161. Juergen Sommer

162. Djibril Diawara (2001)

163. Arnar Gunnlaugsson

164. Carsten Fredgaard

165. Bruce Rioch (1994)

166. Emmanuele Morini

167. French

168. Bo Hansen (Denmark) and Birkir Kristinsson (Iceland)

169. Dwight Pezzarossi

170. Mark Fish (1997)

MIXED BAG - 2

171. Nat Lofthouse (1968-70 and 1971)

172. TSB

173. Joe Smith

174. Phil Neal

175. 6th

176. George Eastham

177. Harold Blackmore

178. Bolton Olympic

179. 90

180. Michael Ricketts (2001-02 – 42 appearances, 15 goals)

FORMER AWAY GROUNDS

181. Manchester City
182. Leicester City
183. Arsenal
184. Middlesbrough
185. Wimbledon
186. Brighton and Hove Albion
187. Coventry City
188. Southampton
189. Reading
190. Derby County

LEGEND - JAY-JAY OKOCHA - 1

191. Augustine Azuka "Jay-Jay" Okocha
192. 2002
193. Nigerian
194. Paris Saint-Germain
195. Borussia Neunkirchen
196. Everton
197. 1993
198. Hull City
199. 145 (124 league, five FA Cup, nine League Cup and seven in Europe)
200. Qatar SC

GARY SPEED

201. Leeds United (in 1988)
202. 2004
203. Newcastle United
204. The First Division Championship (the last ever)
205. Everton
206. West Ham United
207. £5.5m

208. 85

209. 2004

210. Sheffield United

THE HISTORY – 4

211. Clocks

212. 11 (1886, 1891, 1912, 1922, 1925, 1927, 1932, 1934, 1948, 1988 and 1990)

213. West Ham United (32 of Bolton's 35 players signed-up, the other three were too young)

214. Claret and Blue (Burnley, who traditionally played in Claret and Blue, strangely wore all white)

215. Food

216. Ron Bolton (he appeared 12 minutes into the game when Bolton were already 1-0 down and was named Man of the Match)

217. Bill Shankly

218. Manchester United (3-2 on aggregate)

219. Chelsea (Bolton won 2-1)

220. Three

THE BOSS – 1

221. Colin Todd (Wanderers manager 1996-99, Dalglish said: "He was very intelligent")

222. Stan Anderson (Wanderers manager 1980-81)

223. Roy McFarland (Wanderers joint-manager with Colin Todd in 1995-96)

224. Liverpool (1976-86 and Wanderers manager 2007)

225. The Football League War Cup

226. Ian Greaves (Wanderers manager 1974-80)

227. Jimmy Armfield (Wanderers manager 1971-74 – he played for Blackpool from 1954-71 making 627 appearances in all competitions)

228. Joe Smith

229.   Pele

230.   John McGovern (Wanderers manager 1982-85)

SEASON 2006-07 – I

231.   Kevin Davies

232.   Charlton Athletic (2-0 on 26 August)

233   .Walsall

234   .Gary Speed & Ivan Campo

235   .Manchester United

236.   Abdoulaye Faye

237.   Chelsea

238.   Liverpool

239.   Arsenal

240.   Portsmouth (in the Premier League on 30 December 2006)

MIXED BAG - 3

241.   Derby County

242.   Stig Tofting (Wanderers 2002-03, he announced his international retirement following the defeat to England)

243.   3rd

244.   Nat Lofthouse (30 goals)

245.   Jay-Jay Okocha

246.   Sheffield United

247.   Albert Shepherd

248.   Peter Shilton

249.   The Welsh national team

250.   16

MR CONSISTENCY - 2

251.	Michael Johansen, 61	1999-2000
252.	Charlie Wright, 56	1971-72
253.	Jason McAteer, 62	1993-94
254.	David Felgate, 59	1990-91

255.	Jossi Jaaskelainen, 38	2002-03
256.	Chris Fairclough, 54	1996-97
257.	Simon Farnworth, 57	1984-85
258.	Roy Hartle, 45	1963-64
259.	Tal Ben Haim, 49	2005-06
260.	John Higgins, 49	1957-58

THE HISTORY – 5

261. Savings Certificates
262. 1943-44
263. Ray Westwood
264. Bobby Langton
265. Charlton Athletic
266. Walter Rowley
267. Bill Sproston
268. Ray Parry
269. Huddersfield Town
270. Fog

BIG SAM ALLARDYCE - I

271. Limerick
272. West Bromwich Albion
273. Millwall
274. 198 (184 first spell and 14 second spell with the club)
275. Tampa Bay Rowdies
276. Blackpool
277. Coventry City
278. Preston North End
279. Panorama
279. Glastonbury

THE HISTORY – 6

281. Manchester Football Association

282. Notts County

283. Goodison Park (home to Everton)

284. Notts County became the first Second Division team to win the FA Cup

285. Preston North End

286. Everton (in the opening home game of the 1895-96 season)

287. 1898-99

288. Sheffield Wednesday

289. He had not been registered by the club with the Football League

290. Bolton was fined one guinea

NATIONALITIES

291.	Hunt, Nicky	England
292.	Anelka, Nicolas	France
293.	Giannakopoulos, Stelios	Greece
294.	Kazimierczak, Przemysław	Poland
295.	O'Brien, Andy	Republic of Ireland
296.	Wilhelmsson, Christian	Sweden
297.	Diouf, El Hadji	Senegal
298.	Smith, Johann	USA
299.	Braaten, Daniel	Norway
300.	Bogdan, Adam	Hungary

SHERPA VAN TROPHY WINNERS 1988-89

301. Preston North End (won 1-0 at home) and Bury (lost 1-0 away)

302. Preston North End

303. Wrexham

304. Bolton Wanderers 3 Wrexham 1

305. Mark Winstanley

306. Crewe Alexandra

307. Blackpool

308. Bolton 2 Blackpool 1 (1-0 at home and 1-1 away after extra time)

309. Torquay United

310. Wembley Stadium

FRANK WORTHINGTON - I

311. 1977 (September)

312. Leicester City

313. Huddersfield Town

314. Stoke City (on 1 October 1977, Division Two)

315. 1974 (on 15 May in a 1-1 home win over Northern Ireland)

316. 84 (81 + 3 as substitute)

317. 1979 (November)

318. Birmingham City

319. Eight

320. 35

BOLTON WANDERERS v BURNLEY

321. 57

322. 59

323. 27

324. 16

325. Eight

326. Bolton Wanderers 7 Burnley 0

327. 2000-01 (League Division One)

328. The Football League (the inaugural First Division)

329. Joe Smith (nine League and two FA Cup)

330. Associate Members' Cup

SEASON 2005-06 – I

331. Kevin Davies

332. Everton (1-0 on 21 August 2005)

333. West Ham United

334. Abdoulaye Faye and Stelios Giannakopoulos

335. Wigan Athletic

336. Arsenal

337. Kevin Nolan

338. Liverpool

339. West Ham United

340. Ricardo Vaz Te

BIG SAM ALLARDYCE - 2

341. 1973

342. The Second Division Championship with Bolton Wanderers in season 1977-78

343. 1980

344. Sunderland

345. Huddersfield Town

346. Limerick

347. Preston North End (1992)

348. Wolverhampton Wanderers

349. 1985

350. 1999

THE BOSS – 2

351. Manchester City

352. Bill Ridding (in 1968)

353. Charles Foweraker (1923, 1926 and 1929)

354. Walter Rowley (1944-50)

355. Bill Ridding (Wanderers manager 1950-68)

356. Jimmy McIlroy (Wanderers manager 1970)

357. Colin Todd

358. Plymouth Argyle (1977-79)

359. York City

360. Brian Talbot

PLAYERS – 2

361. Ryan Giggs (Manchester United)

362. Birmingham City

363. Stig Tofting (Wanderers 2002-03)

364. Scott Jamieson

365. Frank Worthington (he also scored twice in the 3-0 home win)

366. Radhi Ben Abdelmajid Jaidi

367. Peter Shilton

368. Free Transfer

369. Jack Milton

370. Peter Reid

FA CUP RUNNERS-UP 1952-53

371. Bill Ridding

372. Blackpool

373. Stanley Matthews (The Matthews Final)

374. Fulham

375. Notts County

376. Luton Town

377. Gateshead

378. Everton

379. Maine Road (Manchester City's ground at the time)

380. Blackpool 4 Bolton Wanderers 3

MIXED BAG – 4

381. Notts County

382. Stig Tofting

383. Roy McFarland (Wanderers joint-manager with Colin Todd in 1995-96)

384. 3rd Round (United won 2-1 at Old Trafford on 6 January 1962)

385. Robert Sissons

386. 175 (118 goals in 245 appearances)

387. Nine

388. 16th

389. 1990

390.   Phil Neal

DIVISION 2 CHAMPIONS – 1908-09

391.   Tottenham Hotspur (Spurs won the First Division and FA Cup in
        season 1960-61)
392.   Billy Hughes
393.   Blackpool (they beat Bolton Wanderers 4-3 in the 1953 FA Cup
        Final)
394.   Derby County (Champions in 1971-72 & 1974-75)
395.   24 (W24, D4, L10)
396.   Birmingham City
397.   Stockport County
398.   Bradford Park Avenue and Glossop North End (Preston North
        End finished the 1908-09 season 10th in Division One)
399.   Leeds City
400.   Stokes, David (Bobby Stokes scored for Southampton in their
        1-0 win over Manchester United)

FREIGHT ROVER TROPHY RUNNERS-UP 1985-86

401.   Crewe Alexandra and Stockport County
402.   Tranmere Rovers (2-1 at Burnden Park)
403.   Darlington
404.   Tony Caldwell and George Oghani
405.   Wigan Athletic
406.   Bolton Wanderers 3 Wigan Athletic 1
407.   Bristol City
408.   Bristol City 3 Bolton Wanderers 0
409.   Wembley Stadium
410.   Asa Hartford

ASA HARTFORD

411.   1985 (July)
412.   Norwich City

413.   Division 3

414.   Rotherham United (at home on 17 August 1985)

415.   Stockport County (at home on 20 August 1985)

416.   League Cup (1st Round, 1st leg)

417.   101 (83 League, six FA Cup, four League Cup and eight others)

418.   1987 (June)

419.   Stockport County

420.   Manchester City

MIXED BAG – 5

421.   Radhi Ben Abdelmajid Jaidi

422.   Wanderers became the first club in the Premier League to announce a price reduction (10%) of their season ticket prices for the following season

423.   1986-87

424.   Phil Neal

425.   17th

426.   Malcolm Barrass

427.   £1m

428.   Sam Allardyce (Notts County 1997-99)

429.   Roy McFarland and Colin Todd (Wanderers joint-manager in 1995-96, Todd manager from 1996-99)

430.   Two

2007-08 PRE-SEASON FRIENDLIES

431.   Hibernian

432.   Tranmere Rovers

433.   Espanyol

434.   Ricardo Vaz-Te

435.   Colchester United

436.   Seongnam Ihwa (a 1-1 draw on 12 July 2007)

437.   Zoltan Harsanyi and Kevin Nolan

438.   Racing Santander

439. Nicolas Anelka

440. Olympique Lyonnaise

THE FOREIGN LEGION - 2

441. Tadeusz Nowak (who was signed from Polish club Gornick Zagreb)

442. Dusan Nikolic

443. Fredi Bobic

444. Richard Sneekes and Fabian De Freitas

445. Australia (Sydney)

446. Gudni Bergsson (Iceland) and Sasa Curcic (Yugoslavia)

447. Per Frandsen and Michael Johansen

448. Swiss

449. Franck Passi

450. Con Boutsianis

BETWEEN THE STICKS

451. Jim McDonagh (his kick upfield bounced straight over his opposite number Billy O'Rourke)

452. Steve Banks

453. Dave Felgate, Kevin Rose, Andy Dibble and Ally Maxwell

454. Tommy Wright

455. Juergen Sommer

456. Russell Hoult

457. Martyn Margetson

458. Mark Walton

459. Aidan Davison

460. Newcastle United

PLAYERS - 3

461. Chris Armstrong & David Holdsworth

462. Nine

463. £1.2m

464. Nicky Southall (Nottingham Forest, Gillingham and Grimsby Town – League One, Gillingham, Grimsby Town & Norwich City – The Championship, Bolton Wanderers – Premier League)

465. He claimed he couldn't understand the local dialect!

466. Jason McAteer (£4.5m in September 1995)

467. Gordon Taylor

468. They all scored on their debut

469. David Dunn (he re-joined Blackburn Rovers)

470. Owen Coyle

THE BOSS – 3

471. Sammy Lee (Wanderers manager 2007)

472. Everton

473. Phil Neal

474. Bruce Rioch (Wanderers manager 1992-95)

475. Tranmere Rovers

476. Alan Ball

477. Roy McFarland (joint-manager with Colin Todd in 1995-96)

478. Swindon Town

479. George Mulhall (Wanderers manager 1981-82)

480. Jimmy Armfield (Wanderers manager 1971-74)

MIXED BAG – 6

481. Dean and David Holdsworth

482. LED advertising boards (located on the perimeter of the Nat Lofthouse Stand)

483. Phil Neal

484. 8th

485. They only played one game each for the Trotters

486. Matt Clarke

487. Kevin Nolan & Gary Speed

488. 1982 (John McGovern was appointed player-manager)

489. Alan Thompson (Aston Villa), Sasa Curcic (Aston Villa), Nathan

Blake   (Blackburn Rovers), Eidur Gudjohnsen (Chelsea), Claus
         Jensen (Charlton Athletic) and Jason McAteer (Liverpool)
490.   Elvis Presley

MAIDEN EUROPEAN ADVENTURE

491.   The FA Cup winners entered the European Cup Winners' Cup
         (up to season 1998-99 and the UEFA Cup thereafter) but the
         competition was not inaugurated until season 1960-61.
492.   2005-06 (UEFA Cup)
493.   Lokomotiv Plovdiv (on 15 September 2005 at the Reebok)
494.   Bulgaria
495.   Bolton Wanderers 2 Lokomotiv Plovdiv 1
496.   El Hadji Diouf (in the 2-1 win over Lokomotiv Plovdiv)
497.   Aleksander Tunchev scored an own goal (Kevin Nolan scored
         Bolton's second goal in the 2-1 win)
498.   Besiktas, Sevilla, Vitoria Guimaraes Zenit and St. Petersburg
499.   3rd Round
500.   Olympique Marseilles (drew 1st leg at home 0-0 and lost the
away   leg 2-1)

NAMED AND NUMBERED

501.   1995-96 (after being promoted to the Premier League)
502.   Keith Branagan
503.   Sasa Curcic and Jason McAteer
504.   John McGinlay and John Salako
505.   Kevin Wolze
506.   Steve Banks
507.   No.22 (he has retained this number ever since)
508.   Bob Taylor
509.   No.23
510.   Dean Holdsworth

PLAYERS - 4

511. Steve McManaman

512. Paris Saint-Germain (European Cup Winners' Cup) and Inter Milan (UEFA Cup)

513. 74

514. Tom and John Buchan

515. 12

516. Stig Tofting (Wanderers 2002-03)

517. Chesterfield

518. Oldham Athletic

519. Ali Al-Habsi (from Oman)

520. Fulham

KEVIN DAVIES

521. 2003 (23 July)

522. Southampton

523. Chesterfield (1993-97)

524. Manchester United (in a 4-0 defeat at Old Trafford on 16 August 2003)

525. Blackburn Rovers

526. £7.25m

527. Blackburn Rovers (in a 2-2 Premier League draw at the Reebok on 23 August 2003)

528. Millwall (nine League games, three League goals)

529. Southampton (1997-98 and 2000-03)

530. FA Cup in 2002-03 (awarded by Southampton for services to the club en route to the final) and League Cup in 2003-04 (with Bolton Wanderers)

IVAN CAMPO

531. 2002 (he moved permanently at the start of the 2002-03 season)

532. Real Madrid

533. Deportivo Alaves

534. Manchester United (as a substitute in a 1-0 win at Old Trafford on 11 September 2002)

535. Real Valladolid

536. Valencia CF

537. Liverpool (on 14 September 2002 in a 3-2 Premier League loss at the Reebok)

538. Real Mallorca (RCD Mallorca)

539. Pelos (Hairs)

540. Centre Half

PLAYERS 2007-08 - 2

541. Andranik Teymourian (Iran)

542. It means "son of Helga", Helga is the Christian name of the player's mother

543. Gavin McCann

544. Daniel Braaten

545. Lubomír Michalík

546. Scott Jamieson (Australia)

547. Robert Sissons

548. Zoltan Harsányi

549. Mikel Alonso

550. Olympique Marseilles

MIXED BAG – 7

551. Chris Armstrong (Wanderers 2002)

552. 7th

553. Mascot of the Season

554. Danny Guthrie

555. They all scored two goals for Bolton Wanderers on their debut

556. Mark Kinsella (on 25 April 1997 in a game the Trotters won 4-1)

557. Steve Banks

558. Simon Darby

559. 1999 (Sam Allardyce was appointed)

560.   Les Ferdinand (he became a qualified helicopter pilot after taking an interest in the hobby during his playing days at Newcastle United)

LEGEND – NAT LOFTHOUSE – 2

561.   Yugoslavia (in a 2-2 draw at Arsenal Stadium)
562.   1961 (on 10th July)
563.   He was made a Freeman of Bolton
564.   1958
565.   Club President (since 1986)
566.   30
567.   The East Stand
568.   OBE
569.   255 (285 overall in all competitions)
570.   Uruguay

YOURI DJORKAEFF

571.   2002
572.   1.FC Kaiserlautern
573.   Grenoble Foot 38
574.   Southampton (in a 0-0 draw away to Southampton on 23 February 2002)
575.   RS Strasbourg (1989-91), AS Monaco (1991-95) and Paris Saint-Germain (1995- 96)
576.   Inter Milan
577.   Charlton Athletic
578.   2004
579.   Blackburn Rovers
580.   The 1998 FIFA World Cup, the 2000 European Championships and the 2001 FIFA Confederation Cup

THE BOSS – 4

581.   Sam Allardyce (Wanderers manager 1999-2007)

582. Bill Ridding (1950-68)

583. Arsenal (1995-96)

584. Colin Todd (Wanderers manager 1996-99)

585. Jimmy Armfield (Wanderers manager 1971-74)

586. John McGovern (then at Nottingham Forest and Wanderers manager 1982-85)

587. 14

588. Jimmy McIlroy ("The Jimmy McIlroy Stand", he played for Burnley from 1950-62 and managed Wanderers in 1970)

589. Newcastle United

590. Bruce Rioch

BURNDEN PARK - 2

591. The FA Cup Final (Tottenham Hotspur beat Sheffield United 3-1)

592. Stoke City

593. 33

594. The Ministry of Supply

595. 69,912

596. Manchester City

597. Chesterfield

598. Wimbledon

599. Scott Green (in Bolton's 3-2 defeat to Chesterfield in the FA Cup)

600. Manchester United

PLAYERS - 5

601. Nat Lofthouse (255), Joe Smith (254), David Jack (144), Jack Milsom (142), Ray Westwood (127), Willie Moir (118), John Byrom (113), Harold Blackmore (111) and Neil Whatmore (107)

602. Jay-Jay Okocha

603. £525,000

604. Chris Armstrong (he scored in a 1-1 Premier League draw on 23

September 1997)

605. £11m

606. Johan Elmander

607. Jon Otsemobor

608. Michael Bridges (from Leeds United)

609. James and Richard Turner

610. Seven

FINAL APPEARANCES – 2

611.	FA Cup Final	1926
612.	Sherpa Van Trophy Final	1989
613.	FA Cup Final	1953
614.	Lancashire Cup Final	1948
615.	Freight Rover Trophy Final	1986
616.	FA Cup Final	1929
617.	Lancashire Cup Final	1912
618.	Peace Cup Final	2007
619.	FA Cup Final	1958
620.	Lancashire Cup Final	1886

PLAYERS - 6

621. Manchester City

622. Ivan Campo

623. Sam Allardyce

624. Aidan Davison

625. They all cost the club over £1m

626. Sheffield

627. Trigger

628. John McGinlay

629. Chris Armstrong (Wanderers 2002)

630. Stig Tofting (Wanderers 2002-03)

631. They missed every one of them
632. He was the first Bolton player to be sent off in a competitive game (he swore at the referee who awarded a goal that Sutcliffe claimed never crossed the line)
633. Burnley and Preston North End
634. Liverpool
635. The cycling track
636. £6,472
637. Netherlands
638. West Bromwich Albion
639. The Great Lever Stand (it was given a roof)
640. £1300

SEASON 2005-06 – 2

641. Leicester City
642. Watford (The Hornets)
643. Manchester United (at Old Trafford)
644. Manchester City
645. Stelios Giannakopoulos
646. Wigan Athletic (2-0 away on 20 December 2005)
647. 53
648. Kevin Davies
649. Middlesbrough 4 Bolton Wanderers 3
650. Radhi Jaïdi

BOLTON IN THE 1970s

651. It was the youngest ever Bolton team to take to the pitch for a competitive game (the team was selected by Nat Lofthouse)
652. Jimmy McIlroy
653. They were relegated to Division Three
654. Fences (following problems with crowd invasions)
655. Warwick Rimmer

656. Frank Worthington (he had his back to goal at the edge of the 18 - yard box, superbly controlling the ball with his knee before flicking it over his head, turning and volleying it past the goalkeeper)

657. It was the first game to be played on a Sunday by English League clubs

658. Bobby Moore (Bolton's Mike Walsh made it 2-2 in the fifth minute of injury time and when the referee blew for full-time three minutes later he was surrounded by the Fulham players complaining about his time keeping)

659. Neil McNab

660. Wilf McGuinness (Manchester United manager from April-December 1969)

WINNERS – 2

661.	Football League Second Division	1978
662.	Football League First Division	1997
663.	Lancashire Cup	1948
664.	Sherpa Van Trophy	1989
665.	FA Cup	1926
666.	Football League Third Division	1973
667.	Central League (Reserves)	1955
668.	FA Premier League Asia Trophy	2005
669.	Reserve League North (Reserves)	2007
670.	Lancashire Cup	1925

LEGEND - JAY-JAY OKOCHA - 2

671. 2007

672. BBC African Player of the Year

673. Fenerbahce SK

674. Three (1994, 1998 & 2002)

675. "Jay-Jay. So Good They Named Him Twice"

676. An Olympic gold medal in football at the Atlanta Games

677. Jay-Jay claimed that God told him to sign for Hull City

678. Eintracht Frankfurt

679. 18 (14 League and four League Cup)

680. "Superskills with Jay-Jay Okocha"

SEASON 2006-07 – 2

681. Doncaster Rovers

682. Kevin Davies (El Hadji Diouf and Nicolas Anelka also scored)

683. Kevin Nolan

684. Charlton Athletic (a 1-0 away defeat on 25 October 2006)

685. Kevin Nolan

686. West Ham United (a 3-1 away defeat in the penultimate Premier League game of the season)

687. 18

688. El Hadji Diouf (in a 1-1 Premier League draw away to Fulham in the second game of the season)

689. Middlesbrough (Kevin Nolan scored)

690. Aston Villa

THE BOSS – 5

691. Stanley Matthews

692. Colin Todd (Derby County & Wanderers manager from 1996-99)

693. Bruce Rioch (Wanderers manager 1992-95)

694. John McGovern (Wanderers manager 1982-85)

695. Sammy Lee (Wanderers manager 2007)

696. Oxford United

697. Jimmy Armfield (Wanderers manager 1971-74)

698. Shrewsbury Town

699. Roy McFarland (Wanderers joint-manager with Colin Todd in 1995-96)

700. October

THE HISTORY – 8

701.   Gerry Taggart

702.   18

703.   1995-96

704.   Ralph and Tommy Banks

705.   16th

706.   Bob Struthers, James Cassidy and Tony Caldwell

707.   Nat Lofthouse

708.   7-2 (at Old Trafford on 18 January 1958, Division One)

709.   Mixu Paatelainen

710.   He was the scorer of Bolton's first ever goal at Burnden Park when he opened the scoring in the Division 1 game with Everton on 14 September 1895

MIXED BAG – 8

711.   Bobby Charlton, Gary Lineker, Jimmy Greaves and Michael Owen

712.   Tom Mather

713.   8th

714.   Belfast (Belfast Distillery)

715.   Jay-Jay Okocha

716.   Sammy Lee

717.   Lofty the Lion

718.   Phil Neal

719.   Thailand

720.   Asa Hartford (Wanderers 1985-87)

BIG SAM ALLARDYCE - 3

721.   Notts County

722.   Four Four Two (on amateur football management, coaching and tactics)

723.   Newcastle United

724.   Preston North End

725.   3rd place (season 1995-96)

726.   Notts County

727.   2007

728.   Newcastle United

729.   21

730.   Limerick (1991-92) and Bolton Wanderers (1999-2007)

PLAYERS – 7

731.   Stig Tofting

732.   Chelsea

733.   Jermaine Johnson

734.   Kevin Davies (for Chesterfield)

735.   Michael Ricketts

736.   Chris Basham

737.   Bo Hansen (Bolton lost 4-0)

738.   Hidetoshi Nakata

739.   Ali Al-Habsi

740.   Kevin Davies (he scored against Blackburn Rovers and
        Southampton)

THE BOSS – 6

741.   Roy McFarland (Wanderers joint-manager with Colin Todd in
        1995-96)

742.   Jimmy Armfield (Wanderers manager 1971-74)

743.   Bruce Rioch (Wanderers manager 1992-95)

744.   Stoke City

745.   Bradford City

746.   Charlie Wright (Wanderers manager 1984-85)

747.   Jimmy McIlroy (Wanderers manager 1970)

748.   Huddersfield Town

749.   Charles Foweraker – 25 years (1919-44)

750.   Middlesbrough

PLAYERS 2007-08 - I

751. Ian Walker
752. Heidar Helguson
753. Nicky Hunt
754. Christian Wilhelmsson
755. Gavin McCann
756. Ricardo Vaz Tê (Portugal)
757. Blerim Džemaili (he is actually Swiss but of Albanian origin)
758. Joey O'Brien
759. Ľubomír Michalík (for Slovakia)
760. James Sinclair

THE HISTORY - 9

761. Aston Villa
762. Railwaymen
763. No offside from throw ins
764. £2500
765. Joe Smith
766. Manchester City
767. The Lancashire Cup
768. David Jack
769. Ray Westwood
770. Harold Blackmore

EL HADJI-DIOUF

771. 2005 (he was only on loan in season 2004-05)
772. 23
773. Manchester United (in a 2-2 draw at the Reebok on 11 September 2004)
774. Liverpool
775. Newcastle United (in a 2-1 Premier League win at the Reebok on 31 October 2004)
776. RC Lens

777. Nine

778. 2000

779. He scored the club's first ever goal at home in one of the three major European competitions (the UEFA Cup versus Lokomotiv Plovdiv)

780. Sunderland

NICOLAS ANELKA

781. Fenerbahce Spor Kulubu

782. 2006

783. Paris Saint-Germain

784. Liverpool

785. Arsenal

786. Real Madrid

787. 35 apps, 11 goals

788. The PFA Young Player of the Year Award

789. Arsenal (he scored twice in the game)

790. Kevin Keegan (for Manchester City in 2002)

TAL BEN HAIM

791. Israel

792. Maccabi Tel Aviv

793. 2004

794. 88

795. 2007

796. One

797. Ligat ha'Al (the Israeli Premier League)

798. 2002

799. Besiktas

800. £150,000

THE BOSS – 7

801. Bruce Rioch (Wanderers manager 1992-95)

802. John McGovern (Wanderers manager 1982-85)

803. George Mulhall (Wanderers manager 1981-82)

804. Ian Greaves (Wanderers manager 1974-80)

805. Jimmy Armfield (then at Blackpool and later Wanderers manager 1971-74)

806. Jack Charlton

807. Phil Brown

808. Southend

809. Jimmy Armfield (then a Blackpool player and later Wanderers manager 1971-74)

810. Derby County (2001-02)

FREDI BOBIC

811. Borussia Dortmund

812. 2002

813. 16 (includes two as a substitute)

814. Stuttgarter Kickers

815. Hannover 96

816. Four

817. 37

818. Socialist Federal Republic of Yugoslavia

819. 1995-96 (with Vfb Stuttgart)

820. NK Rijeka

PLAYERS – 8

821. £750,000

822. Radhi Ben Abdelmajid Jaidi (Tunisia)

823. Bill McAdam

824. Frank Worthington

825. Kevin Davies

826. Ali Al-Habsi

827. Youri Djorkaeff (Wanderers 2002-04)

828. Zoltan Harsányi (Slovakia)

829. James Sinclair

830. Przemysław Kazimierczak

BOLTON IN THE 1980s

831. 1986-87

832. Mike Walsh

833. Neil Whatmore

834. Brian Kidd (a European Cup winner with Manchester United in 1968)

835. Season 1985-86, Rotherham United on 17 August 1985

836. Tony Caldwell (in a 1-1 draw with Rotherham United at Burnden Park on 17 August 1985)

837. Cardiff City

838. George Mulhall

839. Wayne Foster

840. Tony Caldwell

PER FRANDSEN

841. 1996

842. 1999

843. Blackburn Rovers

844. 271

845. 2000-01

846. Midfielder

847. 32

848. Wigan Athletic

849. Boldklubben 1903

850. 23

RICARDO GARDNER

851. Harbour View

852. Left Midfield/Left Back

853. 1998

854.	30

855.	14-years old

856.	West Bromwich Albion

857.	1998

858.	Dancehall

859.	The captaincy of the Jamaican national football team

860.	The 1998 FIFA World Cup Finals in France

THE HISTORY – 10

861.	Alan Thompson

862.	Dean and David Holdsworth

863.	Charlton Athletic who brought on Keith Peacock for Michael
Rose	in a game at Burnden Park which Wanderers won 4-2

864.	HB Electronics

865.	He was the first player Bolton Wanderers paid a transfer fee for
	(£3,500)

866.	Nat Lofthouse OBE, Peter Shilton OBE and an MBE, Roger
	Hunt OBE, Peter Beardsley MBE and Les Ferdinand MBE

867.	Kevin Nolan

868.	It was the last ever 50,000 crowd seen at Burnden Park

869.	Coca-Cola

870.	Preston North End

STELIOS GIANNAKOPOULOS

871.	Stylianos Giannakopoulos

872.	2003

873.	Olympiacos

874.	Ethnikos Asteras (1992-93)

875.	Paniliakos

876.	31 appearances, two League goals

877.	Manchester United

878.	1997

879.	The 2004 European Football Championships

880. Stelios has the distinction of being part of the substitution that holds the record of the largest difference between the number of letters in the surnames of two players in a Premier League substitution, 12 letters (14 in Giannakopolous and two in Ba)

JUSSI JAASKELAINEN
881. Finnish
882. 1997
883. Vaasan Palloseura (VPS)
884. £100,000
885. BWFC Fans' "Player Of The Year Award" and BWFC "Players' Player Of The Year Award"
886. 1998 (on 25 March 1998 versus Malta)
887. Liverpool
888. Colin Todd
889. Crystal Palace
890. 2001-02

PLAYERS – 9
891. Youri Djorkaeff
892. Legia Warsaw
893. Harold Hassall and John Wheeler
894. Andy Walker
895. The 2006 African Cup of Nations
896. Sam Ashton
897. Con Boutsianis
898. Peter Beardsley, Peter Reid and Peter Shilton
899. Mikel Alonso (his brother Xabi Alonso played for Liverpool)
900. Jlloyd Samuel (with Aston Villa)

EIDUR GUDJOHNSEN
901. 1998
902. 59

903. Iceland
904. PSV Eindhoven
905. 2000
906. Chelsea
907. FC Barcelona
908. 27
909. Birmingham City
910. £4m

JOHN McGINLAY

911. 1992
912. 195
913. Millwall
914. 1997
915. 87
916. Bradford City
917. 13
918. Cincinnati Riverhawks
919. Oldham Athletic
920. Nairn County, North Shore United, Yeovil Town, Elgin City, Shrewsbury Town and Bury

PLAYERS – 10

921. Ali Al-Habsi
922. Andranik Teymourian
923. Stig Tofting (Wanderers 2002-03)
924. Jlloyd Samuel
925. Heidar Helguson
926. Nicky Hunt
927. Abdoulaye Méïté
928. Christian Wilhelmsson
929. Hull City
930. Gavin McCann

HENRIK PEDERSEN

931. 2001
932. Silkeborg IF
933. 2007
934. Hull City
935. 143
936. Carpenter
937. Leicester City
938. 22
939. Silkeborg IF
940. His peacock goal celebration (a style he developed with his former Danish international team mate Martin Retov)

FRANK WORTHINGTON - 2

941. Tranmere Rovers
942. "One Hump or Two"?
943. Southampton
944. Mjällby AIF
945. 1988
946. Stockport County
947. Two (in his eight appearances)
948. Sunderland
949. Leicester City (210)
950. 234

THE MANAGEMENT GAME

951. Sam Allardyce   Blackpool
952. Asa Hartford   Shrewsbury Town
953. Tommy Wright   Linfield
954. Peter Barnes   Runcorn
955. Len Cantello   Oldham Town
956. Stuart Gray   Southampton
957. Brian Kidd   Blackburn Rovers

958.	Peter Shilton	Plymouth Argyle
959.	John McGinlay	Grestley Rovers
960.	Neil McNab	Exeter City

BOLTON WANDERERS v MANCHESTER UNITED

961.	55
962.	25
963.	6-1 (at Burnden Park on 3 January 1914, Division One)
964.	1979-80 (United won 2-0 at home and 3-1 away)
965.	Six (four wins, one draw and one defeat)
966.	Two (Premier League/First Division and Second Division)
967.	Manchester United 1 Bolton Wanderers 0
968.	1995-96 (United won 3-0 at home and 6-0 at Bolton)
969.	1978-79 (at Burnden Park on 22 December 1978, First Division)
970.	Bolton Wanderers 3 Manchester United 0

MR CONSISTENCY - 3

971.	John Hulme, 40	1970-71
972.	Bryan Edwards, 44	1955-56
973.	Michael Ricketts, 42	2001-02
974.	Keith Branagan, 60	1992-93
975.	Jim McDonagh, 47	1982-83
976.	Eddie Hopkinson, 50	1960-61
977.	Kevin Nolan, 42	2004-05
978.	Claus Jensen, 54	1998-99
979.	Phil Brown/Julian Darby, 62	1989-90
980.	Jimmy Phillips, 45	1995-96

PHIL NEAL

981.	1985 (December)
982.	64
983.	Northampton Town
984.	Six

985. Cardiff City

986. European Cup Winners' Cup

987. Wales

988. The Sherpa Van Trophy

989. 50

990. Graham Taylor

PLAYERS IN – SEASON 2007-08

991.	Zoltan Harsanyi	FC Senec
992.	Gerald Cid	Bordeaux
993.	Blerim Dzemaili	FC Zurich
994.	Danny Guthrie	Liverpool
995.	Mikel Alonso	Real Sociedad
996.	Heidar Helguson	Fulham
997.	Christian Wilhelmsson	Nantes
998.	Adam Bogdan	Vasas
999.	Daniel Braaten	Rosenborg
1000.	Andy O'Brien	Portsmouth

NOTES:

NOTES:

NOTES:

NOTES:

NOTES:

NOTES:

NOTES:

www.apexpublishing.co.uk